Better Homes and Gardens®

Eat Healthy Lose Weight

Volume 6

Meredith® Consumer Marketing
Des Moines, Iowa

Better Homes and Gardens.

Eat Healthy Lose Weight

MEREDITH CONSUMER MARKETING

Vice President, Consumer Marketing: Janet Donnelly
Consumer Product Marketing Director: Heather Sorensen
Consumer Product Marketing Manager: Amanda Werts
Business Director: Ron Clingman
Senior Production Manager: Al Rodruck

WATERBURY PUBLICATIONS, INC.

Editorial Director: Lisa Kingsley
Associate Editor: Tricia Bergman
Creative Director: Ken Carlson
Associate Design Directors: Doug Samuelson
Production Assistant: Mindy Samuelson
Contributing Copy Editors: Terri Fredrickson, Gretchen Kauffman
Contributing Indexer: Elizabeth T. Parson

BETTER HOMES AND GARDENS. MAGAZINE

Editor in Chief: Gayle Goodson Butler
Senior Deputy Editor, Food & Entertaining: Nancy Wall Hopkins

MEREDITH NATIONAL MEDIA GROUP
President: Tom Harty

MEREDITH CORPORATION
Chairman and Chief Executive Officer: Stephen M. Lacy

In Memoriam: E.T. Meredith III (1933–2003)

Better Homes and Gardens. Test Kitchen

Our seal assures you that every recipe in *Eat Healthy, Lose Weight* Vol. 6 has been tested in the Better Homes and Gardens® Test Kitchen. This means that each recipe is practical and reliable and meets our high standards of taste appeal. We guarantee your satisfaction with this book for as long as you own it.

All of us at Meredith Consumer Marketing are dedicated to providing you with information and ideas to enhance your home. We welcome your comments and suggestions. Write to us at: Meredith Consumer Marketing, 1716 Locust St., Des Moines, IA 50309-3023.

Pictured on front cover:
Grilled Flank Steak Salad, page 78

Contents

4 Introduction

5 Snacks

23 Breakfast

52 Sandwiches

75 Main-Dish Salads

92 Meat

130 Poultry

157 Fish

179 Vegetarian

193 Soups

215 Sides

239 Sweets

263 Index & Metric

EAT GREAT, FEEL GREAT

The recipe for losing weight is to change the way that you eat for life—no gimmicks or fad diets. And all of the foods you need to eat healthfully, forestall cravings, and shed excess weight are in your local supermarket—and in this book. Wholesome ingredients plus healthful cooking methods equal the perfect weight loss equation. The recipes in *Eat Healthy, Lose Weight* Vol. 6 rely on lean proteins, whole grains, and fresh fruits and vegetables for delicious meals your family will love.

The guideline used to create the more than 200 recipes in this book is simple: Use ordinary ingredients to create extraordinary recipes that are lower in fat, calories, and sodium. The recipes were created for people living in the real world! And each recipe was tested by the Better Homes and Gardens. Test Kitchen, so you can be assured that these recipes are simple to follow, they work, and they taste great. If food doesn't taste good, you don't want to eat it— no matter how good it is for you. If you want to lose weight, your goal in changing the way you eat is to stick to a plan that staves off boredom, encourages discipline, and is both satisfying and delicious.

The recipes in *Eat Healthy, Lose Weight* are perfect for everyday family meals (and special occasions) that everyone will look forward to—from company-special appetizers to hearty casseroles to desserts that taste indulgent but stay well within calorie and fat guidelines. You'll find recipes such as Chicken, Macaroni, and Cheese; Grilled Chili Burgers; Roast Pork with Romesco Sauce; Shrimp Po' Boys; and Lemon Tart with Ginger-Oat Crust that are specially developed to fit a healthy-eating plan—recipes that will help you live healthier without sacrificing flavor.

Change your diet and change your life!

Snacks

Bourbon-Glazed Cocktail Sausages

PREP: 10 minutes
SLOW COOK: 4 hours (low)

NUTRITION FACTS
PER SERVING

Calories 86
Fat 2 g
Cholesterol 24 mg
Sodium 285 mg
Carbohydrates 7 g
Fiber 0 g
Protein 8 g

16 ounces light cooked smoked
    Polish sausage or smoked
    turkey sausage, cut into 1-inch
    slices
⅓ cup low-sugar apricot
    preserves
3 tablespoons pure maple syrup
1 tablespoon bourbon or water
1 teaspoon quick-cooking
    tapioca, crushed

1. In a 1½-quart slow cooker combine sausage slices, apricot preserves, maple syrup, bourbon, and tapioca. Cover and cook on low-heat setting for 4 hours. If no heat setting is available, cook for 4 hours.

2. Serve immediately or keep warm in the slow cooker for up to 1 hour. **MAKES 12 SERVINGS**

Five-Spice Chicken Wings

PREP: 20 minutes
BAKE: 20 minutes
SLOW COOK: 3 hours (low) or 1½ hours (high)
OVEN: 375°F

NUTRITION FACTS PER SERVING

Calories 32
Fat 1 g
Cholesterol 9 mg
Sodium 45 mg
Carbohydrates 3 g
Fiber 0 g
Protein 3 g

16 chicken wings (about 3 pounds)
¾ cup bottled plum sauce
1 tablespoon butter, melted
1 teaspoon five-spice powder
   Slivered green onions (optional)

1. Preheat oven to 375°F. Using a sharp knife, carefully cut off tips of the wings; discard wing tips. Cut each wing at joint to make 2 pieces.

2. In a foil-lined 15×10×1-inch baking pan arrange wing pieces in a single layer. Bake for 20 minutes. Drain well.

3. In a 3½- or 4-quart slow cooker combine plum sauce, butter, and five-spice powder. Add chicken pieces, stirring to coat with sauce.

4. Cover and cook on low-heat setting for 3 to 4 hours or on high-heat setting for 1½ to 2 hours.

5. Serve immediately or keep warm, covered, on warm- or low-heat setting for up to 1 hour. If desired, sprinkle with slivered green onions. **MAKES 32 SERVINGS**

Honey, Pear, and Gorgonzola Crostini

PREP: 15 minutes   BROIL: 1½ minutes

NUTRITION FACTS PER SERVING

Calories 76   *Fat* 2 g   *Cholesterol* 5 mg   *Sodium* 185 mg   *Carbohydrates* 1 g   *Fiber* 1 g   *Protein* 3 g

16 ½-inch-thick slices baguette-style French bread
1   ripe pear, halved, cored, and very thinly sliced
2   tablespoons flavored honey (such as French lavender honey) or regular honey
4   ounces Gorgonzola cheese or other blue cheese, crumbled
    Snipped fresh chives (optional)

1. Preheat broiler. On a large ungreased baking sheet arrange bread slices. Broil 4 inches from heat for 1½ to 2 minutes or until lightly toasted, turning once.

2. Halve pear slices; place on bread slices. Lightly drizzle with honey. Top with cheese and, if desired, chives. Serve immediately.
MAKES 16 SERVINGS

Spicy Black Bean Crab Cakes

PREP: 25 minutes
COOK: 6 minutes

NUTRITION FACTS PER SERVING

Calories 107
Fat 4 g
Cholesterol 27 mg
Sodium 138 mg
Carbohydrates 2 g
Fiber 2 g
Protein 9 g

½ cup refrigerated or frozen egg product, thawed, or 2 eggs, lightly beaten
⅓ cup light sour cream
½ cup whole wheat panko (Japanese-style bread crumbs)
1 clove garlic, minced
¾ cup canned no-salt-added black beans, rinsed and drained
1 6- to 6.5-ounce can crabmeat, drained and flaked
1 jalapeño, seeded and finely chopped*
¼ cup frozen whole kernel corn, thawed
¼ cup seeded and finely chopped tomato
1 tablespoon canola oil
1 recipe Lime-Onion Cream
Cilantro leaves (optional)

1. In a large bowl combine egg and sour cream. Stir in panko and garlic. Mash ½ cup of the black beans and leave ¼ cup whole. Add mashed and whole beans to panko mixture along with crab, jalapeño, corn, and tomato. Mix well. Shape mixture into eight ¾-inch-thick patties.

2. In a very large nonstick skillet heat oil over medium heat. Add crab cakes; cook for 6 to 8 minutes or until golden brown and heated through, turning once. If crab cakes brown too quickly, reduce heat to medium-low.

3. Serve crab cakes immediately with Lime-Onion Cream. If desired, garnish with cilantro leaves. **MAKES 8 SERVINGS**

Lime-Onion Cream: In a small bowl stir together ⅓ cup light sour cream, 2 tablespoons bottled chunky salsa, 1 tablespoon thinly sliced green onion, 1 teaspoon fat-free milk, and ½ teaspoon finely shredded lime peel.

*Note: Because hot chile peppers, such as jalapeños, contain volatile oils that can burn your skin and eyes, avoid direct contact with chiles as much as possible. When working with chile peppers, wear plastic or rubber gloves. If your bare hands do touch the chile peppers, wash your hands well with soap and water.

Smoky Nut-Stuffed Apricots

PREP: 30 minutes
BAKE: 8 minutes
OVEN: 375°F

NUTRITION FACTS PER SERVING

Calories 105
Fat 6 g
Cholesterol 20 mg
Sodium 243 mg
Carbohydrates 2 g
Fiber 1 g
Protein 4 g

16 dried apricots
2   ounces provolone cheese, cut into 16 small cubes
⅛   teaspoon cayenne pepper (optional)
8   pecan or walnut halves, toasted and halved
8   slices turkey bacon, cooked according to package directions

1. Preheat oven to 375°F. Cut a slit in the side of each apricot; gently pull apricot open at the slit. In a small bowl toss together provolone cheese cubes and, if desired cayenne pepper. Place a cheese piece and a pecan piece into each apricot. Press apricots back together.

2. Cool bacon slightly; cut each slice in half lengthwise. Wrap 1 bacon piece around each stuffed apricot. Use wooden toothpicks to secure.

3. Arrange bacon-wrapped apricots on a greased or parchment paper-lined baking sheet. Bake about 8 minutes or until heated through and cheese is softened. Serve warm. **MAKES 8 SERVINGS**

Walnut and Olive Quesadillas

PREP: 20 minutes   BAKE: 10 minutes   OVEN: 350°F

NUTRITION FACTS PER SERVING

Calories 98   *Fat* 6 g   *Cholesterol* 9 mg   *Sodium* 217 mg   *Carbohydrates* 8 g   *Fiber* 1 g   *Protein* 5 g

6 6-inch white or yellow corn tortillas
4 ounces part-skim mozzarella cheese, shredded (1 cup)
2 ounces provolone cheese, shredded (½ cup)
¼ cup chopped pitted ripe olives
3 tablespoons chopped walnuts or pine nuts, toasted (see note, page 46)
2 teaspoons snipped fresh oregano or ½ teaspoon dried oregano, crushed
1 tablespoon olive oil
½ cup purchased mild salsa
1 teaspoon snipped fresh oregano or ¼ teaspoon dried oregano, crushed
   Fresh oregano sprigs (optional)

1. Preheat oven to 350°F. Stack tortillas and wrap in foil. Bake about 10 minutes or until softened. Meanwhile, in a medium bowl combine mozzarella cheese, provolone cheese, olives, nuts, and the 2 teaspoons snipped oregano or ½ teaspoon dried oregano. Spread cheese mixture onto half of each tortilla. Fold tortillas in half; secure with wooden toothpicks. Brush one side of each quesadilla with some of the oil.

2. In a large skillet or on a griddle place quesadillas, 2 or 3 at a time, oiled sides down; cook over medium heat about 4 minutes or until heated through, brushing with remaining oil and turning once. Cut each quesadilla in half.

3. Meanwhile, in a small saucepan heat salsa just until hot; stir in the 1 teaspoon snipped oregano. If desired, garnish with oregano sprigs. Serve with quesadillas.
MAKES 4 SERVINGS

Sweet Party Mix

PREP: 20 minutes
BAKE: 20 minutes
BAKE: 300°F

NUTRITION FACTS PER SERVING

Calories 74
Fat 2 g
Cholesterol 3 mg
Sodium 106 mg
Carbohydrates 1 g
Fiber 1 g
Protein 1 g

Nonstick cooking spray
4   cups bite-size corn square cereal
3   cups bite-size rice square cereal
2   cups pretzel knots
⅔   cup sliced almonds
½   cup packed brown sugar
¼   cup butter
2   tablespoons light-color corn syrup
⅛   teaspoon baking soda
¾   cup dried cranberries, blueberries, or cherries

1. Preheat oven to 300°F. Lightly coat a large piece of foil with cooking spray; set aside. In a large roasting pan toss together corn cereal, rice cereal, pretzels, and almonds; set aside.

2. In a medium saucepan combine brown sugar, butter, and corn syrup. Cook and stir over medium heat until mixture just begins to bubble. Continue cooking at a moderate, steady rate, without stirring, for 5 minutes more. Remove saucepan from heat; stir in baking soda. Pour over cereal mixture; stir gently to coat.

3. Bake for 15 minutes; stir cereal mixture and bake 5 minutes more. Remove from oven; stir in dried fruit. Spread on prepared foil to cool. Store in an airtight container.
MAKES 36 SERVINGS

Watermelon, Mango, and Jicama Salsa

START TO FINISH: 30 minutes

NUTRITION FACTS PER SERVING

Calories 126
Fat 1 g
Cholesterol 0 mg
Sodium 201 mg
Carbohydrates 28 g
Fiber 2 g
Protein 3 g

3   cups chopped, seeded watermelon
1½ cups peeled and chopped jicama
1   cup peeled and chopped mango
2   tablespoons chopped green onion (1)
1   jalapeño, seeded and finely chopped (see note, page 10)
1   tablespoon snipped fresh cilantro
1   tablespoon lime juice
⅛   teaspoon cayenne pepper
    Baked tortilla chips

1. In a medium bowl combine watermelon, jicama, mango, green onion, jalapeño, cilantro, lime juice, and cayenne pepper.

2. If desired, cover and chill for up to 24 hours. Serve salsa with tortilla chips or with chicken, pork, or fish. **MAKES 24 SERVINGS**

Rio Grande Dip

PREP: 20 minutes   SLOW COOK: 3 hours

NUTRITION FACTS PER SERVING

Calories 76   *Fat* 2 g   *Cholesterol* 5 mg   *Sodium* 258 mg   *Carbohydrates* 12 g   *Fiber* 2 g   *Protein* 4 g

4   ounces uncooked Italian turkey sausage links, casings removed if needed
½   of an onion, finely chopped
1   15-ounce can reduced-fat refried black beans
¾   cup shredded reduced-fat Monterey Jack cheese (3 ounces)
¾   cup bottled salsa
½   of a 4-ounce can diced green chiles, undrained
2   tablespoons shredded reduced-fat Monterey Jack cheese (optional)
1   9-ounce bag scoop-shape baked tortilla chips

1. In a medium skillet crumble sausage and cook with onion over medium-high heat until meat is browned, stirring to break up sausage as it cooks. Drain off fat. Transfer meat mixture to a 1½-quart slow cooker. Stir in refried beans, the ¾ cup cheese, the salsa, and chiles.

2. Cover and cook on low-heat setting for 3 to 4 hours. If no heat setting is available, cook for 3 to 4 hours.

3. Stir well before serving. Serve immediately or keep warm, covered, on warm- or low-heat setting (if available) for up to 2 hours. If desired, sprinkle with the 2 tablespoons cheese. Serve dip with tortilla chips.
MAKES 24 SERVINGS

Pine Nut–White Bean Dip

PREP: 15 minutes
CHILL: 2 hours

NUTRITION FACTS PER SERVING

Calories 40
Fat 1 g
Cholesterol 1 mg
Sodium 70 mg
Carbohydrates 7 g
Fiber 2 g
Protein 3 g

¼ cup soft bread crumbs
2 tablespoons fat-free milk
1 15-ounce can white kidney beans (cannellini beans) or Great Northern beans, rinsed and drained
¼ cup fat-free or light sour cream
3 tablespoons pine nuts, toasted
¼ teaspoon salt-free garlic and herb seasoning blend or other salt-free seasoning blend
⅛ teaspoon cayenne pepper
2 teaspoons chopped fresh oregano or basil or
½ teaspoon dried oregano or basil, crushed
Pine nuts, toasted (see note, page 46) (optional)
Fresh oregano or basil leaves (optional)
Assorted vegetables

1. In a small bowl combine bread crumbs and milk. Cover and let stand for 5 minutes.

2. Meanwhile, in a blender or food processor combine beans, sour cream, the 3 tablespoons pine nuts, the seasoning blend, and cayenne pepper. Cover and blend or process until nearly smooth. Add bread crumb mixture. Cover and blend or process until smooth. Stir in chopped or dried oregano or basil. Cover and chill for 2 hours.

3. If desired, sprinkle with additional pine nuts and garnish with basil or oregano leaves. Serve with assorted vegetable dippers. **MAKES 12 SERVINGS**

Breakfast

Sweet Potato and Turkey Sausage Hash

PREP: 25 minutes
BAKE: 20 minutes
OVEN: 400°F

NUTRITION FACTS PER SERVING

Calories 170
Fat 5 g
Cholesterol 33 mg
Sodium 493 mg
Carbohydrates 22 g
Fiber 3 g
Protein 10 g

2 russet potatoes, peeled, if desired, and diced

1 sweet potato, peeled, if desired, and diced
Nonstick cooking spray

½ of a 14-ounce ring smoked turkey sausage, halved lengthwise and sliced ½ inch thick

¾ cup chopped green sweet pepper (1 medium)

½ cup chopped onion (1 medium)

1 tablespoon snipped fresh sage or 1 teaspoon dried sage, crushed

¼ teaspoon black pepper

1. Preheat oven to 400°F. Place russet and sweet potatoes on a 15×10×1-inch baking sheet. Lightly coat with cooking spray and toss to coat.

2. Bake 20 minutes or until tender and lightly browned, turning once with a spatula.

3. Meanwhile, in a large nonstick skillet cook sausage, sweet pepper, and onion for 8 to 10 minutes or until tender. Stir in sweet potato mixture, sage, and black pepper.
MAKES 4 SERVINGS

Baked Eggs with Roasted Vegetables

PREP: 25 minutes
ROAST:
CHILL: 8 hours
STAND: 30 minutes
BAKE: 15 minutes
OVEN: 425°F/375°F

NUTRITION FACTS PER SERVING

Calories 232
Fat 12 g
Cholesterol 218 mg
Sodium 332 mg
Carbohydrates 21 g
Fiber 4 g
Protein 11 g

3   cups small broccoli florets (about 1 inch in size)

12   ounces yellow potatoes, such as Yukon gold, cut into ½- to ¾-inch pieces (about 2 cups)

1   sweet potato, cut into ½- to ¾-inch pieces (about 1 cup)

1   red onion, cut into thin wedges

2   tablespoons olive oil

¼   teaspoon salt

6   eggs

½   cup shredded Manchego cheese, (2 ounces)

½   teaspoon cracked black pepper

1. Preheat oven to 425°F. Coat a 2-quart rectangular baking dish with nonstick cooking spray. In a large bowl combine broccoli, yellow potatoes, sweet potato, onion, olive oil, and salt, tossing to coat vegetables.

2. Spread vegetable mixture evenly in the prepared pan. Roast for 10 minutes. Stir vegetables; roast about 5 minutes more or until vegetables are tender and starting to brown. Remove from oven. Spread vegetables evenly in baking dish; cool. Cover and chill in the refrigerator for 8 to 24 hours.

3. Let chilled vegetables stand at room temperature for 30 minutes. Meanwhile, preheat oven to 375°F.

4. Bake vegetables, uncovered, for 5 minutes. Remove from oven; make 6 wells in the layer of vegetables. Break an egg into each well. Bake for 5 minutes more. Sprinkle with cheese. Bake for 5 to 10 minutes more or until eggs whites are set and yolks are starting to thicken. Sprinkle with pepper. **MAKES 6 SERVINGS**

Poached Eggs on Soft Polenta

START TO FINISH: 30 minutes

NUTRITION FACTS PER SERVING

Calories 218   *Fat* 9 g   *Cholesterol* 220 mg   *Sodium* 319 mg   *Carbohydrates* 3 g   *Fiber* 2 g   *Protein* 12 g

1   cup water
¼   teaspoon salt
1   cup fat-free milk
½   cup cornmeal
¼   cup finely shredded Asiago or Parmesan cheese
2   tablespoons chopped fresh basil or 1 teaspoon dried basil, crushed
4   eggs
1   red onion, thinly sliced
1   teaspoon canola oil
1   grape or cherry tomatoes, halved
¼   teaspoon cracked black pepper
¼   cup fresh basil and/or arugula leaves (optional)

1. In a small saucepan bring the water to boiling. Meanwhile, in a medium bowl combine cornmeal, milk, and salt. Slowly add cornmeal mixture to boiling water, stirring constantly. Cook and stir until mixture returns to boiling. Reduce heat to low. Cook for 10 to 15 minutes or until mixture is thick, stirring frequently. Stir in cheese and dried basil if using. Place in a serving bowl; keep warm.

2. Lightly grease a large skillet. Half-fill skillet with water. Bring the water to boiling; reduce heat to simmering (bubbles should begin to break the surface of the water). Break 1 of the eggs into a measuring cup. Holding the lip of the cup as close to the water as possible, carefully slide egg into simmering water. Repeat with remaining eggs, allowing each egg an equal amount of space. Simmer eggs, uncovered, for 3 to 5 minutes or until the whites are completely set and yolks begin to thicken but are not hard. Remove eggs with a slotted spoon.

3. In a large skillet cook onion in hot oil over medium heat for 5 minutes or until tender. Stir in tomatoes and cook stirring, 2 minutes more or until they begin to soften. Sprinkle with pepper.

4. Serve polenta topped with poached eggs and tomato mixture. If desired, garnish with fresh basil and/or arugula. **MAKES 4 SERVINGS**

Baked Eggs with Tomato

PREP: 20 minutes
BAKE: 16 minutes
OVEN: 350°F

NUTRITION FACTS PER SERVING

Calories 107
Fat 6 g
Cholesterol 214 mg
Sodium 231 mg
Carbohydrates 2 g
Fiber 0 g
Protein 12 g

1   roma tomato, finely chopped (⅓ cup)
1   tablespoon finely chopped green onion
1   tablespoon snipped fresh cilantro
1   teaspoon finely chopped jalapeño (see note, page 10)
1   teaspoon lime juice
⅛   teaspoon salt
    Nonstick cooking spray
4   egg whites
4   eggs
4   tablespoons fat-free milk
¼   teaspoon black pepper
2   tablespoons finely shredded reduced-fat cheddar cheese

1. Preheat oven to 350°F. For tomato topper, in a small bowl combine tomato, green onion, cilantro, jalapeño, lime juice, and salt; set aside.

2. Spray four 8-ounce ramekins with cooking spray. Place an egg white in each dish. Top each with a whole egg, positioning the yolk in the center of the ramekin. Add 1 tablespoon milk to each ramekin. Top evenly with black pepper, then cheese. Place ramekins on a baking sheet.

3. Bake, uncovered, for 16 to 18 minutes or until eggs are set around edges but still a little jiggly in the center. Top each serving evenly with the tomato topper.
MAKES 4 SERVINGS

Bacon and Egg Breakfast Wraps

START TO FINISH: 25 minutes

NUTRITION FACTS PER SERVING

Calories 195
Fat 9 g
Cholesterol 11 mg
Sodium 462 mg
Carbohydrates 18 g
Fiber 1 g
Protein 11 g

4   slices bacon, chopped
1   cup chopped fresh
    mushrooms
1   green sweet pepper, chopped
    (½ cup)
¼   teaspoon chili powder
¼   teaspoon black pepper
⅛   teaspoon salt
1   cup refrigerated or frozen egg
    product, thawed
¼   cup chopped, seeded tomato
    Few drops bottled hot pepper
    sauce
4   8-inch flour tortillas, warmed
    (see note, page 34)

1. In a large nonstick skillet cook bacon over medium heat until crisp. Using a slotted spoon, remove bacon from skillet, reserving 1 tablespoon of the drippings in the skillet (discard the remaining drippings). Drain bacon on paper towels.

2. Add mushrooms, sweet pepper, chili powder, black pepper, and salt to the reserved drippings in skillet; cook and stir about 3 minutes or until vegetables are tender.

3. Pour egg over vegetable mixture in skillet. Cook over medium heat. As mixture sets, run a spatula around edge of skillet, lifting and folding egg mixture so the uncooked portion flows underneath. Continue cooking over medium heat about 2 minutes or until egg is cooked through but still glossy and moist. Stir in cooked bacon, tomato, and hot pepper sauce. Divide egg mixture among tortillas; roll up tortillas. To serve, cut wraps in half.
MAKES 4 SERVINGS

Breakfast Pita Pizza

PREP: 20 minutes   BAKE: 8 minutes   OVEN: 375°F

NUTRITION FACTS PER SERVING

Calories 256   *Fat* 11 g   *Cholesterol* 20 mg   *Sodium* 417 mg   *Carbohydrates* 24 g   *Fiber* 4 g   *Protein* 15 g

½ cup sliced fresh mushrooms
1 red or green sweet pepper, chopped (½ cup)
1 teaspoon olive oil
3 ounces firm tub-style tofu (fresh bean curd), drained and crumbled (about ½ cup)
1 green onion, thinly sliced
1 clove garlic, minced
⅛ teaspoon black pepper
1 whole wheat pita bread round, split horizontally
½ cup shredded reduced-fat cheddar cheese (2 ounces)

1. Preheat oven to 375°F. In a medium skillet cook mushrooms and sweet pepper in hot oil over medium heat for 5 to 8 minutes or until tender, stirring occasionally. Stir in tofu, green onion, garlic, and black pepper.

2. Place pita halves, cut sides down, on a baking sheet. Sprinkle pita halves with ¼ cup of the cheese. Top with mushroom mixture. Sprinkle the remaining ¼ cup cheese over mushroom mixture on pita halves. Bake for 8 to 10 minutes or until heated through and cheese melts.
MAKES 2 SERVINGS

Poblano Tofu Scramble

PREP: 25 minutes
COOK: 10 minutes

NUTRITION FACTS PER SERVING

Calories 182
Fat 10 g
Cholesterol 0 mg
Sodium 158 mg
Carbohydrates 11 g
Fiber 3 g
Protein 13 g

1   16- to 18-ounce package extra-firm water-packed tofu (fresh bean curd)
1   tablespoon olive oil
1   poblano chile, seeded and chopped (see note, page 10)
½   cup chopped onion (1 medium)
2   cloves garlic, minced
1   teaspoon chili powder
½   teaspoon ground cumin
½   teaspoon dried oregano, crushed
¼   teaspoon salt
1   tablespoon lime juice
2   roma tomatoes, seeded and chopped (about 1 cup)
    Fresh cilantro sprigs (optional)

1. Drain tofu; cut tofu in half and pat each half with paper towels until well dried. Crumble the tofu into a medium bowl. Set aside.

2. In a large nonstick skillet heat olive oil over medium-high heat. Add chopped chile, onion, and garlic; cook and stir for 4 minutes. Add chili powder, cumin, oregano, and salt. Cook and stir for 30 seconds more.

3. Add crumbled tofu to chile pepper mixture. Reduce heat. Cook for 5 minutes, gently stirring occasionally. Just before serving, drizzle with lime juice and fold in tomatoes. If desired, garnish with fresh cilantro. **MAKES 4 SERVINGS**

Sausage Skillet

START TO FINISH: 20 minutes

NUTRITION FACTS PER SERVING

Calories 187
Fat 6 g
Cholesterol 19 mg
Sodium 475 mg
Carbohydrates 28 g
Fiber 4 g
Protein 8 g

1   teaspoon canola oil
2   ounces smoked turkey sausage, cut diagonally into ½-inch slices
1   cup frozen diced hash brown potatoes
½   of a zucchini, halved lengthwise and cut into ½-inch pieces
½   of a red sweet pepper, coarsely chopped
⅓   cup thinly sliced red onion
1   clove garlic, minced
¼   teaspoon chili powder
⅛   teaspoon black pepper
¼   cup bottled salsa

1. In a large nonstick skillet heat oil over medium heat. Add sausage, potatoes, zucchini, sweet pepper, red onion, garlic, chili powder, and black pepper to skillet.

2. Cook for 4 to 5 minutes or until sausage is lightly browned and vegetables are tender, stirring occasionally. Spoon salsa over sausage mixture. **MAKES 2 SERVINGS**

Oatmeal Pancakes with Maple Bananas

PREP: 20 minutes   STAND: 10 minutes   COOK: 2 minutes per batch

NUTRITION FACTS PER SERVING

Calories 159   *Fat* 3 g   *Cholesterol* 1 mg   *Sodium* 246 mg   *Carbohydrates* 1 g   *Fiber* 2 g   *Protein* 5 g

3   bananas, peeled and sliced
½   cup blueberries
¼   cup sugar-free maple-flavor syrup
2   teaspoons lemon juice
¼   teaspoon ground cinnamon
1   cup flour
½   cup quick-cooking rolled oats
1½ teaspoons baking powder
½   teaspoon baking soda
⅛   teaspoon salt
1   cup low-fat buttermilk or sour milk*
¼   cup refrigerated or frozen egg product, thawed, or 1 egg, lightly beaten
1   tablespoon canola oil
1   tablespoon sugar-free maple-flavor syrup
1   teaspoon vanilla

1. For maple bananas, in a medium bowl stir together bananas, blueberries, the ¼ cup syrup, the lemon juice, and cinnamon. Set aside.

2. In a large bowl stir together flour, oats, baking powder, baking soda, and salt. In a medium bowl use a fork to combine buttermilk, egg, oil, the 1 tablespoon syrup, and the vanilla. Add buttermilk mixture all at once to flour mixture. Stir just until moistened. Let stand for 10 minutes to soften oats.

3. Spoon 2 slightly rounded tablespoons batter onto a hot, lightly greased griddle or heavy skillet; spread to a 3- to 4-inch circle. Cook over medium heat for 1 to 2 minutes on each side or until pancakes are golden brown. Turn over when edges are slightly dry and bottoms are browned. Serve warm topped with maple bananas. **MAKES 8 SERVINGS**

*Note: To make 1 cup sour milk, place 1 tablespoon lemon juice or vinegar in a glass measuring cup. Add enough fat-free milk to make 1 cup total liquid; stir. Let the mixture stand for 5 minutes before using.

Citrus Mock Mimosas

PREP: 10 minutes
CHILL: 2 hours

NUTRITION FACTS PER SERVING

Calories 53
Fat 0 g
Cholesterol 0 mg
Sodium 19 mg
Carbohydrates 13 g
Fiber 0 g
Protein 1 g

¾ cup fresh orange juice
½ cup fresh grapefruit juice
¼ cup fresh lime juice
1 to 2 tablespoons honey
1 12-ounce bottle sparkling
   water, chilled
   Long, thin strips of orange
   peel, grapefruit peel, and/or
   lime peel, curled (optional)

1. In a 2-cup glass measure combine orange juice, grapefruit juice, lime juice, and honey. Stir until honey is dissolved. Cover and chill mixture for at least 2 hours or up to 24 hours to blend flavors.

2. To serve, pour juice mixture into four champagne glasses. Add sparkling water and stir lightly to mix. If desired, garnish with citrus peel strips. **MAKES 4 SERVINGS**

Mix and Match Banana Berry Smoothie

START TO FINISH: 15 minutes

NUTRITION FACTS
PER SERVING

Calories 145
Fat 1 g
Cholesterol 0 mg
Sodium 32 mg
Carbohydrates 34 g
Fiber 3 g
Protein 2 g

1   banana, cut up
1   cup blueberries, raspberries,
    blackberries, or strawberries
1   cup frozen unsweetened
    peach slices
½   cup pomegranate, cherry,
    blueberry, or cranberry juice
½   cup low-fat plain or vanilla
    soymilk
1   cup ice cubes
¼   cup low-fat granola
¼   cup blueberries, raspberries,
    blackberries, or strawberries

1. In a blender combine banana, 1 cup berries, peaches, fruit juice, and soymilk. Cover and blend until smooth. With the motor running, add ice cubes, one at a time, through the opening in the lid until combined and slushy. Top servings with granola and the ¼ cup berries. **MAKES 4 SERVINGS**

Sandwiches

Asian Pork Sandwiches

PREP: 25 minutes
SLOW COOK: 10 hours (low) or 5 hours (high)

NUTRITION FACTS PER SERVING

Calories 282
Fat 7 g
Cholesterol 61 mg
Sodium 478 mg
Carbohydrates 27 g
Fiber 3 g
Protein 26 g

1   2.5- to 3-pound pork shoulder roast
1   cup apple juice or apple cider
2   tablespoons reduced-sodium soy sauce
2   tablespoons bottled hoisin sauce
1½ teaspoons five-spice powder
8   whole wheat hamburger buns, split and toasted
2   cups shredded napa cabbage
2   green onions, thinly sliced

1. Trim fat from roast. If necessary, cut roast to fit in a 3½- or 4-quart slow cooker. Place roast in cooker. In a small bowl combine apple juice, soy sauce, hoisin sauce, and five-spice powder. Pour over roast in cooker.

2. Cover and cook on low-heat setting for 10 to 12 hours or on high-heat setting for 5 to 6 hours.

3. Remove meat from cooker, reserving cooking liquid. Remove meat from bone; discard bone. Using two forks, shred meat; discard fat. Place ½ cup meat (about 3 ounces) on each bun bottom. Top with ¼ cup shredded cabbage; add bun tops. Skim fat from cooking liquid. Place 3 tablespoons cooking liquid each in bowls for dipping; sprinkle liquid with green onions.
MAKES 8 SERVINGS

Hot Ham and Pear Melts

PREP: 15 minutes
BAKE: 10 minutes
OVEN: 350°F

NUTRITION FACTS PER SERVING

Calories 300
Fat 10 g
Cholesterol 32 mg
Sodium 647 mg
Carbohydrates 36 g
Fiber 3 g
Protein 16 g

1   10- to 12-ounce whole grain baguette
2   tablespoons lower-sugar apricot preserves
6   ounces thinly sliced lower-sodium cooked ham
1   pear, quartered, cored, and thinly sliced
2   cups arugula or fresh spinach
1   4-ounce package goat cheese (chèvre), softened
1   teaspoon snipped fresh chives
    Nonstick cooking spray

1. Preheat oven to 350°F. Cut baguette crosswise into 4 portions. Split each portion in half horizontally. Scoop out the soft centers of tops and bottoms of baguette portions, leaving about a ½-inch shell. (Save soft bread centers for another use.)

2. Spread preserves on cut sides of bottom halves of baguette portions. Top with ham, pear slices, and arugula. In a small bowl stir together goat cheese and chives; spread on cut sides of the top halves of the baguette portions. Place over arugula, cheese sides down. Lightly coat tops and bottoms of sandwiches with cooking spray.

3. Place sandwiches in a shallow baking pan. Cover with foil. Bake for 10 to 15 minutes or until heated through. Serve warm.
MAKES 4 SERVINGS

Grilled Chili Burgers

PREP: 20 minutes   GRILL: 10 minutes

NUTRITION FACTS PER SERVING

Calories 325   *Fat* 15 g   *Cholesterol* 74 mg   *Sodium* 407 mg   *Carbohydrates* 21 g   *Fiber* 4 g   *Protein* 26 g

1   recipe Chimichurri
1   pound 95% or higher lean ground beef
8   ounces ground pork
1   tablespoon chili powder
½   teaspoon onion powder
¼   teaspoon ground cumin
⅛   teaspoon salt
3   whole wheat pita bread rounds, quartered and toasted
¾   cup bottled roasted red sweet peppers, drained and cut into strips

1. Prepare Chimichurri. Set aside. In a large bowl combine beef, pork, chili powder, onion powder, cumin, and salt. Mix well. Shape into six ½-inch-thick patties.

2. For a charcoal grill, grill patties on the rack of an uncovered grill for 10 to 13 minutes or until an instant-read thermometer inserted into side of each patty registers 160°F, turning once halfway through grilling. (For a gas grill, preheat grill. Reduce heat to medium. Place patties on grill rack over heat. Cover and grill as above.)

3. Place each grilled patty on top of 2 of the pita quarters. Top with roasted peppers and Chimichurri. **MAKES 6 SERVINGS**

Chimichurri: In a small bowl combine ½ cup finely snipped fresh parsley; ½ cup finely snipped fresh cilantro; 2 tablespoons red wine vinegar; 1 tablespoon olive oil; 2 cloves garlic, minced; ¼ teaspoon salt; ¼ teaspoon black pepper; and ⅛ teaspoon cayenne pepper.

Open-Face Shredded Beef Sandwiches

PREP: 25 minutes
SLOWCOOK: 9 hours (low) or 4½ hours (high)

NUTRITION FACTS
PER SERVING

Calories 272
Fat 8 g
Cholesterol 31 mg
Sodium 563 mg
Carbohydrates 2 g
Fiber 4 g
Protein 21 g

1   tablespoon instant espresso coffee granules
1   pound extra-lean boneless chuck roast, trimmed of fat
    Nonstick cooking spray
1½ cups chopped onions (3 medium)
½   of a red sweet pepper, cut into thin bite-size strips
½   of a green sweet pepper, cut into thin bite-size trips
4   cloves garlic, minced
2   dried bay leaves
½   cup dry red wine
2   tablespoons cider vinegar
1   tablespoon Worcestershire sauce
½   teaspoon salt
6   slices multigrain Italian bread (about 1½ ounces each)
6   slices provolone cheese (3 ounces total)

1. Press the coffee granules into both sides of roast. Coat a medium nonstick skillet with cooking spray; heat over medium-high heat. Add roast; cook until light brown on both sides, turning once.

2. Meanwhile, coat a 3- or 3½-quart slow cooker with cooking spray. Layer onions, pepper strips, garlic, and bay leaves in cooker. If necessary, cut roast to fit into cooker. Place roast on top of vegetables.

3. Add wine to skillet; bring to boiling over medium-high heat, scraping browned bits from bottom and sides of skillet. Remove from heat; stir in vinegar and Worcestershire sauce. Pour over roast.

4. Cover and cook on low-heat setting for 9 to 10 hours or on high-heat setting for 4½ to 5 hours.

5. Using a slotted spoon, transfer meat to a cutting board. Remove and discard bay leaves. Add salt to mixture in cooker. Using two forks, pull meat apart into shreds; return to cooker, stirring to combine.

6. Preheat broiler. Arrange bread slices on a baking sheet; top each with a cheese slice. Broil 4 to 5 inches from heat until cheese melts and bread is toasted.

7. To serve, using a slotted spoon, divide meat mixture among bread slices. **MAKES 6 SERVINGS**

Tropical Chicken Salad Wraps

START TO FINISH: 25 minutes

NUTRITION FACTS
PER SERVING

Calories 243
Fat 10 g
Cholesterol 66 mg
Sodium 301 mg
Carbohydrates 14 g
Fiber 1 g
Protein 23 g

2   cups shredded cooked chicken breast
2   cups finely shredded napa cabbage
1   8-ounce can crushed pineapple, drained
⅓   cup light mayonnaise
2   tablespoons flaked coconut, toasted (see note, page 46)
1   tablespoon lime juice
1   tablespoon chopped fresh cilantro
1   teaspoon Jamaican jerk seasoning
8   Bibb or Boston lettuce leaves
    Lime wedges (optional)

1. In a large bowl combine chicken, shredded cabbage, drained pineapple, mayonnaise, coconut, lime juice, cilantro, and Jamaican jerk seasoning.

2. Divide chicken mixture between leaves. Fold in sides and roll up. Secure with toothpicks if needed. If desired, serve with lime wedges. **MAKES 4 SERVINGS**

Italian Meatball Rolls

PREP: 15 minutes   COOK: 12 minutes   BROIL: 2 minutes

NUTRITION FACTS PER SERVING

Calories 344   *Fat* 12 g   *Cholesterol* 70 mg   *Sodium* 644 mg   *Carbohydrates* 36 g   *Fiber* 4 g   *Protein* 21 g

Nonstick cooking spray
2½ cups thinly sliced cremini mushrooms
½ cup chopped onion (1 medium)
2 cloves garlic, minced
1 8-ounce can no-salt-added tomato sauce
2 tablespoons balsamic vinegar
½ teaspoon dried rosemary, crushed
½ teaspoon dried oregano, crushed
8 ounces refrigerated Italian-style cooked turkey meatballs (8 meatballs), halved
4 whole wheat hot dog buns
½ cup shredded part-skim mozzarella cheese (2 ounces)
Snipped fresh oregano (optional)

1. Preheat broiler. Coat an unheated large nonstick skillet with cooking spray; preheat over medium heat. Add mushrooms, onion, and garlic to hot skillet; cook for 5 to 10 minutes or until tender, stirring occasionally. Add tomato sauce, balsamic vinegar, rosemary, and the dried oregano. Bring to boiling; reduce heat. Simmer, covered, for 2 minutes. Stir in meatballs. Cook about 5 minutes more or until meatballs are heated through.

2. Meanwhile, open buns so they lie flat and place on a baking sheet, cut sides up. Broil 4 to 5 inches from the heat about 1 minute or until lightly toasted. Divide meatball mixture among buns. Sprinkle with cheese. Broil for 1 to 2 minutes more or until cheese is melted. If desired, sprinkle with fresh oregano. **MAKES 4 SERVINGS**

Pan Bagnat

START TO FINISH: **20 minutes**

NUTRITION FACTS PER SERVING

Calories 360
Fat 12 g
Cholesterol 134 mg
Sodium 610 mg
Carbohydrates 6 g
Fiber 10 g
Protein 28 g

1   10-ounce loaf whole grain baguette-style French bread, split lengthwise, slightly hollowed out if desired, and toasted
1   tablespoon extra virgin olive oil
2   4.5-ounce packages herb and garlic or lemon pepper marinated chunk light tuna
1   green sweet pepper, cut into thin bite-size strips
1   tomato, thinly sliced
2   hard-cooked eggs, sliced
¼   cup thinly sliced red onion

1. Drizzle cut sides of baguette with olive oil. On the bottom half of baguette place tuna; top with sweet pepper, tomato, eggs, and onion. Top with top half of baguette. Cut crosswise into 4 servings. **MAKES 4 SERVINGS**

Bruschetta Burgers

START TO FINISH: 25 minutes

NUTRITION FACTS
PER SERVING

Calories 178
Fat 5 g
Cholesterol 16 mg
Sodium 538 mg
Carbohydrates 21 g
Fiber 6 g
Protein 17 g

4 frozen tomato-, basil-, and
Parmesan cheese-flavor
meatless burger patties
4 slices mozzarella cheese
(about 3 ounces total)
2 thin multigrain sandwich
rounds or 4 slices whole
wheat bread
8 to 12 fresh basil leaves
4 tomato slices
Shredded fresh basil
(optional)

1. Prepare frozen patties
according to package directions.
Preheat broiler. Arrange cooked
patties on one side of a large
baking sheet. Top with cheese
slices. Separate sandwich rounds
and place, cut sides up, on the
baking sheet with the patties.

2. Broil 4 to 5 inches from the heat
for 1 to 2 minutes or until cheese
is melted and sandwich rounds are
toasted. Divide basil leaves among
sandwich rounds. Top each with a
patty and a tomato slice. If desired,
top with shredded basil.
MAKES 4 SERVINGS

Roasted Vegetable Pitas

PREP: 25 minutes
ROAST: 25 minutes
OVEN: 400°F

**NUTRITION FACTS
PER SERVING**

Calories 225
Fat 9 g
Cholesterol 3 mg
Sodium 448 mg
Carbohydrates 5 g
Fiber 6 g
Protein 8 g

1½ cups coarsely chopped
    Japanese eggplant (1 small)
1¼ cups coarsely chopped
    zucchini (1 small)
1¼ cups coarsely chopped red or
    yellow sweet pepper (1 large)
1 small red onion, cut into
    1-inch chunks (1 cup)
4 cloves garlic, sliced
2 tablespoons olive oil
1 teaspoon dried oregano,
    crushed
¼ teaspoon crushed red pepper
¼ teaspoon salt
1 cup yellow pear or cherry
    tomatoes, halved
1 tablespoon lemon juice
2 whole wheat pita bread
    rounds, halved
¼ cup plain Greek fat-free
    yogurt
¼ cup crumbled reduced-fat feta
    cheese

1. Preheat oven to 400°F. In a large bowl combine eggplant, zucchini, sweet pepper, onion, garlic, olive oil, oregano, crushed red pepper, and salt. Toss to combine. Spread vegetable mixture in a shallow roasting pan. Roast, uncovered, for 15 minutes. Add tomatoes; stir until combined. Roast about 10 minutes more or until vegetables are lightly browned and tender.

2. Drizzle vegetables with lemon juice; toss to coat. Divide vegetable mixture among 4 pita bread halves. Top with yogurt and sprinkle with feta. Serve immediately.
MAKES 4 SERVINGS

CHAPTER 4

Main-Dish Salads

Lemon-Sage Pork Salad

START TO FINISH: 40 minutes

NUTRITION FACTS
PER SERVING

Calories 266
Fat 14 g
Cholesterol 49 mg
Sodium 269 mg
Carbohydrates 8 g
Fiber 7 g
Protein 21 g

1 pound pork tenderloin
1 tablespoon finely shredded lemon peel
6 fresh sage leaves, thinly sliced
½ teaspoon ground cumin
¼ teaspoon black pepper
⅛ teaspoon salt
1 tablespoon olive oil
1 green leaf lettuce, torn
1½ cups chopped tomatoes
1 avocado, halved, seeded, peeled, and chopped
1 cup canned black beans, rinsed and drained
½ cup chopped green onions
1 recipe Red Hot Pepper Vinaigrette

1. Trim fat from pork. Cut pork crosswise into ¼-inch-thick slices. Place pork slices in a large bowl. Add lemon peel, sage, cumin, pepper, and salt. Toss well to coat. Let stand for 10 minutes.

2. In a very large skillet cook pork, half at a time, in hot oil over medium-high heat for 2 to 3 minutes or until meat is just slightly pink in center, turning once. Remove from skillet and set aside.

3. Place lettuce on a serving platter. Top with tomatoes, avocado, beans, and green onions. Arrange pork slices over salad. Drizzle with some Red Hot Pepper Vinaigrette; pass remaining vinaigrette. **MAKES 6 SERVINGS**

Red Hot Pepper Vinaigrette: Preheat oven to 425°F. Halve 1 red sweet pepper and 1 jalapeño (see note, page 10) lengthwise. Remove stems, seeds, and membranes. Place pepper halves, cut sides down, on a foil-lined baking sheet. Bake for 20 to 25 minutes or until skin is blistered and charred. Bring foil up around peppers to enclose. Let stand about 15 minutes or until cool. Use a sharp knife to loosen edges of the skins; gently pull off the skins in strips and discard. Place peppers in a blender or food processor. Add 2 tablespoons lime juice, 2 tablespoons vinegar, 2 tablespoons olive oil, and ⅛ teaspoon salt. Cover and blend or process until smooth.

Pork Barley Salad

PREP: 30 minutes
COOK: 45 minutes
GRILL: 30 minutes
STAND: 10 minutes

NUTRITION FACTS
PER SERVING

Calories 308
Fat 8 g
Cholesterol 49 mg
Sodium 130 mg
Carbohydrates 34 g
Fiber 8 g
Protein 24 g

5   cups water
1   cup pearl barley
1   cup frozen edamame
1   recipe Dijon Vinaigrette
¾   cup chopped red sweet
    pepper (1)
⅓   cup sliced green onions (3)
¼   cup chopped cornichons
¼   cup snipped fresh parsley
1   pound pork tenderloin,
    trimmed
¼   teaspoon black pepper
6   cups Bibb or Boston lettuce
    leaves

1. In a large saucepan bring the water to boiling over high heat. Stir in barley; reduce heat. Cover and simmer for 45 to 50 minutes or just until barley is tender, adding edamame for the last 10 minutes of cooking; drain. Place barley and edamame in a large bowl. Pour Dijon Vinaigrette over warm barley mixture; toss to coat.

2. Add the sweet pepper, green onions, cornichons, and parsley to barley mixture; mix well. Set aside.

3. Sprinkle pork tenderloin with the black pepper. For a charcoal grill, arrange hot coals around a drip pan. Test for medium-high heat above pan. Place meat on grill rack over pan. Cover; grill for 30 to 35 minutes or until a meat thermometer registers 155°F. (For a gas grill, preheat grill. Reduce heat to medium. Adjust for indirect cooking. Grill as directed.)

4. Transfer pork to a cutting board. Cover with foil; let stand for 10 minutes. Cut into ¼-inch-thick slices; cut slices into strips. Add pork to barley mixture; stir to combine. Arrange lettuce on 6 serving plates; spoon warm salad over lettuce. **MAKES 6 SERVINGS**

Dijon Vinaigrette: In a screw-top jar combine ¼ cup white wine vinegar; 2 tablespoons finely chopped red onion; 2 tablespoons olive oil; 2 teaspoons Dijon mustard; 2 cloves garlic, minced; and ¼ teaspoon black pepper. Cover and shake well. Makes about ½ cup.

Grilled Flank Steak Salad

PREP: 30 minutes   **MARINATE:** 30 minutes   **GRILL:** 17 minutes

NUTRITION FACTS PER SERVING

Calories 337   *Fat* 12 g   *Cholesterol* 47 mg   *Sodium* 375 mg   *Carbohydrates* 31 g   *Fiber* 5 g   *Protein* 29 g

1   recipe Cilantro Dressing
8   ounces beef flank steak
2   yellow and/or red sweet peppers, halved
1   ear of fresh sweet corn, husked and silks removed
2   green onions, trimmed
      Nonstick cooking spray
2   cups torn romaine lettuce
4   cherry tomatoes, halved
¼   of a small avocado, peeled and thinly sliced (optional)

1. Prepare Cilantro Dressing and divide it into 2 portions.

2. Trim fat from steak. Score both sides of steak in a diamond pattern by making shallow diagonal cuts at 1-inch intervals. Place steak in a resealable plastic bag set in a shallow dish. Pour 1 portion of the Cilantro Dressing over steak; set remaining dressing portion aside. Seal bag; turn to coat steak. Marinate in the refrigerator for 30 minutes.

3. Coat sweet peppers, corn, and green onions with cooking spray.

4. For a charcoal grill, place steak and corn on the grill rack directly over medium coals. Grill, uncovered, until steak is desired doneness and corn is tender, turning steak once halfway through grilling and turning corn occasionally. For steak, allow 17 to 21 minutes for medium-rare (145°F) to medium (160°F). For corn, allow 15 to 20 minutes. Add sweet pepper halves to the grill for the last 8 minutes of grilling and green onions to the grill for the last 4 minutes of grilling, turning frequently. (For a gas grill, preheat grill. Reduce heat to medium. Place meat and then vegetables on grill rack over heat. Cover and grill as directed.)

5. Thinly slice steak against the grain. Coarsely chop sweet peppers and green onions; cut corn from cob, leaving kernels in "sheets." To serve, divide romaine lettuce between 2 bowls. Place steak, grilled vegetables, tomatoes, and, if desired, avocado slices over romaine. Drizzle salads with the reserved portion of Cilantro Dressing. **MAKES 2 SERVINGS**

Cilantro Dressing: In a blender or small food processor combine 3 tablespoons lime juice; 2 tablespoons chopped shallot; 2 tablespoons snipped fresh cilantro; 1 tablespoon olive oil; 1 tablespoon water; 2 teaspoons honey; 1 large clove garlic, peeled and quartered; ½ teaspoon chili powder; ¼ teaspoon salt; and ¼ teaspoon cumin. Cover and blend or process until combined.

Hot Italian Beef Salad

START TO FINISH: 20 minutes

NUTRITION FACTS PER SERVING

Calories 146
Fat 4 g
Cholesterol 52 mg
Sodium 410 mg
Carbohydrates 6 g
Fiber 1 g
Protein 22 g

1   12-ounce beef top round steak, cut 1 inch thick
    Nonstick cooking spray
1   red or green sweet pepper, seeded and cut into bite-size strips
½   cup bottled fat-free Italian salad dressing
6   cups torn mixed salad greens
¼   cup finely shredded Parmesan cheese (1 ounce)
    Coarsely ground black pepper (optional)

1. Trim fat from steak. Thinly slice steak across the grain into bite-size strips.*

2. Coat an unheated large nonstick skillet with nonstick cooking spray. Preheat over medium-high heat. Add steak and sweet pepper to hot skillet. Cook and stir for 3 to 5 minutes or until steak is desired doneness and sweet pepper is crisp-tender; drain. Add dressing to skillet. Cook and stir until heated through.

3. Divide the salad greens among 4 dinner plates. Top with the beef mixture. Sprinkle with Parmesan cheese and, if desired, black pepper. Serve immediately.
MAKES 4 SERVINGS

*__*Note:__ Partially freeze beef for easier slicing.*

Superfoods Salad

START TO FINISH: **25 minutes**

NUTRITION FACTS PER SERVING

Calories 303
Fat 13 g
Cholesterol 63 mg
Sodium 249 mg
Carbohydrates 22 g
Fiber 3 g
Protein 26 g

⅓ cup raspberry vinegar
2 tablespoons snipped fresh mint
2 tablespoons honey
1 tablespoon canola oil
¼ teaspoon salt
4 cups packaged fresh baby spinach leaves
2 cups chopped cooked chicken breast
2 cups fresh strawberries, hulled and sliced
½ cup fresh blueberries
¼ cup walnuts, toasted and coarsely chopped (see note, page 46)
1 ounce semisoft goat cheese, crumbled
½ teaspoon freshly ground black pepper

1. In a screw-top jar combine vinegar, mint, honey, oil, and salt. Cover and shake well.

2. In a large bowl toss together spinach, chicken, strawberries, blueberries, walnuts, and goat cheese. Transfer to salad plates. Drizzle with vinaigrette and sprinkle with pepper.
MAKES 4 SERVINGS

Roasted Tomato and Mushroom Pasta Salad

PREP: 20 minutes
ROAST: 20 minutes
COOL: 30 minutes
OVEN: 450°F

NUTRITION FACTS PER SERVING

Calories 264
Fat 10 g
Cholesterol 6 mg
Sodium 271 mg
Carbohydrates 35 g
Fiber 4 g
Protein 13 g

8   ounces fresh white mushrooms, sliced
8   ounces grape tomatoes or cherry tomatoes, halved
4   cloves garlic, thinly sliced
2   teaspoons dried oregano, crushed
1   tablespoon olive oil
6   ounces dried whole grain penne pasta
2   tablespoons olive oil
2   tablespoons white wine vinegar
½   teaspoon cracked black pepper
1   15-ounce can cannellini beans (white kidney beans), rinsed and drained
½   cup snipped fresh basil
2   ounces Parmesan cheese, shaved

1. Preheat oven to 450°F. Line a 15×10×1-inch baking pan with foil. Arrange mushrooms and tomato halves, cut sides up, in the prepared pan. Sprinkle with garlic and oregano. Drizzle with 1 tablespoon olive oil. Roast, uncovered, for 20 to 25 minutes or until tomatoes are soft and skins begin to split and mushrooms are lightly browned.

2. Meanwhile, cook pasta according to package directions, lightly salting the pasta water; drain. In a large bowl whisk together 2 tablespoons olive oil, vinegar, and pepper. Add warm pasta to bowl; toss to coat. Let cool to room temperature, stirring occasionally.

3. To pasta mixture, add tomato-mushroom mixture and any drippings from the pan, beans, and basil. Toss to combine. Serve at room temperature on 4 serving plates. Top salads with shaved Parmesan. **MAKES 4 SERVINGS**

CHAPTER 5

Meat

Grilled Beef Tenderloin with Mediterranean Relish

PREP: 25 minutes
GRILL: 40 minutes
STAND: 15 minutes

NUTRITION FACTS PER SERVING

Calories 232
Fat 12 g
Cholesterol 70 mg
Sodium 227 mg
Carbohydrates 6 g
Fiber 2 g
Protein 25 g

1	3- to 4-pound center-cut beef tenderloin roast
2	teaspoons dried oregano, crushed
2	teaspoons cracked black pepper
1½	teaspoons finely shredded lemon peel
½	teaspoon salt
3	cloves garlic, minced
2	Japanese eggplants, halved lengthwise, or 1 small eggplant, sliced
2	red or yellow sweet peppers, halved lengthwise and seeded
1	sweet onion (such as Walla Walla or Vidalia), cut into ½-inch slices
1	tablespoon olive oil
⅔	cup chopped roma tomatoes (2 medium)
2	tablespoons chopped pitted kalamata olives
2	tablespoons snipped fresh basil
1	tablespoon balsamic vinegar
¼	teaspoon salt
⅛	teaspoon black pepper

1. Trim fat from meat. For rub, in a small bowl stir together oregano, cracked pepper, lemon peel, the ½ teaspoon salt, and 2 of the garlic cloves. Sprinkle mixture evenly over meat; rub in with your fingers. Brush eggplants, sweet peppers, and onion with oil.

2. For a charcoal grill, arrange hot coals around a drip pan. Test for medium-hot heat above pan. Place meat on grill rack over drip pan. Place vegetables around edge of grill rack directly over coals. Cover and grill for 10 to 12 minutes or until vegetables are tender, turning once halfway through grilling. Remove vegetables from grill. Cover and continue grilling meat for 30 to 40 minutes more or until medium-rare (140°F). (For a gas grill, preheat grill. Reduce heat to medium-high. Adjust for indirect cooking. Grill as above.)

3. Remove meat from grill. Cover with foil; let stand for 15 minutes. (The meat's temperature will rise 5°F during standing.)

4. Meanwhile, for relish, coarsely chop grilled vegetables. In a medium bowl combine grilled vegetables, the remaining 1 garlic clove, tomatoes, olives, basil, vinegar, ¼ teaspoon salt, and ground pepper. Slice meat. Serve meat with relish. **MAKES 12 SERVINGS**

Saucy Pot Roast with Noodles

PREP: 25 minutes
SLOW COOK: 8 hours (low) or
4 hours (high)

NUTRITION FACTS PER SERVING

Calories 324
Fat 7 g
Cholesterol 73 mg
Sodium 586 mg
Carbohydrates 2 g
Fiber 3 g
Protein 31 g

1   2- to 2.5-pound beef chuck
     pot roast
     Nonstick cooking spray
2   medium carrots, sliced
2   stalks celery, sliced
1   medium onion, sliced
2   cloves garlic, minced
1   tablespoon quick-cooking
     tapioca
1   14.5-ounce can Italian-style
     stewed tomatoes, undrained
1   6-ounce can Italian-style
     tomato paste
¼   teaspoon black pepper
1   bay leaf
4   cups hot cooked noodles
     Celery leaves (optional)

1. Trim fat from roast. If
necessary, cut roast to fit into a
3½- or 4-quart slow cooker. Coat a
large nonstick skillet with cooking
spray; heat over medium heat.
Brown roast on all sides in hot
skillet.

2. In the cooker combine carrots,
celery, onion, and garlic. Sprinkle
tapioca over vegetables. Place roast
on top of vegetables.

3. In a medium bowl combine
undrained tomatoes, tomato paste,
pepper, and bay leaf; pour over the
roast in cooker.

4. Cover and cook on low-heat
setting for 8 to 10 hours or on
high-setting for 4 to 5 hours.

5. Discard bay leaf. Cut meat into
serving-size portions. Serve with
hot cooked noodles. If desired,
garnish with celery leaves.
MAKES 8 SERVINGS

Grilled New York Strip Steaks

PREP: 15 minutes   STAND: 20 minutes   GRILL: 12 minutes

NUTRITION FACTS PER SERVING

Calories 302   *Fat* 9 g   *Cholesterol* 95 mg   *Sodium* 418 mg   *Carbohydrates* 1 g   *Fiber* 0 g   *Protein* 50 g

1	tablespoon snipped fresh rosemary
3	cloves garlic, minced
½	teaspoon salt
½	teaspoon cracked black pepper
4	ounces beef top loin steaks (New York strip steaks)
	Finely shredded lemon peel (optional)
	Fresh rosemary sprigs (optional)

1. In a small bowl combine snipped rosemary, garlic, the salt, and pepper. Sprinkle mixture evenly over all sides of steaks; rub in with your fingers. Let stand at room temperature for 20 minutes.

2. For a charcoal grill, arrange medium-hot coals around a drip pan. Place steaks on grill rack directly over coals (not over pan). Grill about 4 minutes or until grill marks are visible, turning once to mark both sides. (For a gas grill, preheat one side of grill; leave burners off on the other side. Reduce heat to medium-high. Place steaks on grill rack over lit burner. Cover and grill as above.)

3. Turn steaks over again, turning meat 90 degrees. Grill about 2 minutes more or until diamond-shape grill marks are visible. Turn over and grill about 2 minutes more or until diamond-shape grill marks are visible on second side.

4. Once cross marks have formed on each side, move steaks away from direct heat and place in a hanging basket or on unheated part of grill (not over coals or heat).

5. Cover and grill until desired doneness. Allow 4 to 8 minutes more for medium-rare (145°F) or 8 to 12 minutes more for medium (160°F). Serve immediately. If desired, sprinkle with lemon peel. If desired, garnish with rosemary sprigs. **MAKES 4 SERVINGS**

Moroccan Beef and Pumpkin Bake

PREP: 30 minutes
BAKE: 20 minutes
OVEN: 400°F

NUTRITION FACTS PER SERVING

Calories 298
Fat 11 g
Cholesterol 72 mg
Sodium 362 mg
Carbohydrates 5 g
Fiber 2 g
Protein 19 g

1 pound 95% lean ground beef
2 cups ½-inch pieces peeled pumpkin or winter squash
¾ cup coarsely chopped red sweet pepper (1 medium)
½ cup coarsely chopped onion (1 medium)
2 cloves garlic, minced
1 cup frozen whole kernel corn
½ cup couscous
1 recipe Moroccan Spice Blend
1 cup lower-sodium beef broth
½ of a 8-ounce package reduced-fat cream cheese (Neufchâtel), cut up
½ cup yellow cornmeal
⅓ cup all-purpose flour
1 tablespoon sugar
1¼ teaspoons baking powder
½ cup fat-free milk
1 egg, beaten
2 tablespoons olive oil
 Snipped fresh mint (optional)
 Pumpkin seeds or sliced almonds, toasted (see note, page 46)(optional)

1. Preheat oven to 400°F. In a large nonstick skillet or a skillet coated with nonstick cooking spray cook ground beef, pumpkin, sweet pepper, onion, and garlic over medium heat until meat is browned and onion is tender, using a wooden spoon to break up meat as it cooks. Drain off fat. Stir corn, couscous, and Moroccan Spice Blend into meat mixture in skillet. Heat through. Add broth and cream cheese, stirring until well mixed. Transfer mixture to 2-quart rectangular baking dish.

2. In a medium bowl combine cornmeal, flour, sugar, baking powder, and ¼ teaspoon salt. In a small bowl whisk together milk, egg, and oil. Add milk mixture to cornmeal mixture all at once. Stir just until moistened. Pour batter over beef mixture in dish.

3. Bake about 20 minutes or until toothpick inserted into topper comes out clean. If desired, garnish with mint and pumpkin seeds.
MAKES 8 SERVINGS

Moroccan Spice Blend: In a small bowl stir together 1 teaspoon ground cumin, ½ teaspoon ground coriander, ½ teaspoon ground ginger, ¼ teaspoon salt, and ⅛ teaspoon ground cinnamon.

Sesame Ginger Beef Stir-Fry

START TO FINISH: 30 minutes

NUTRITION FACTS PER SERVING

Calories 255
Fat 7 g
Cholesterol 36 mg
Sodium 212 mg
Carbohydrates 25 g
Fiber 4 g
Protein 23 g

12 ounces beef sirloin
1 cup reduced-sodium chicken broth
1 tablespoon grated fresh ginger or 1 teaspoon ground ginger
1 tablespoon cornstarch
2 cloves garlic, minced
1 teaspoon ground coriander
⅛ to ¼ teaspoon crushed red pepper
2 teaspoons sesame oil
1 onion, halved and sliced
2 cups broccoli florets
1 red sweet pepper, cut into bite-size strips
1⅓ cups hot cooked brown rice
1 teaspoon sesame seeds, toasted (see note, page 46) (optional)

1. If desired, partially freeze beef for easier slicing. Trim fat from meat. Thinly slice meat across the grain into bite-size strips. Set aside.

2. For sauce, in a small bowl stir together chicken broth, ginger, cornstarch, garlic, coriander, and crushed red pepper; set aside.

3. In a wok or large skillet heat sesame oil over medium-high heat. Add onion and cook and stir in hot oil for 2 minutes. Add broccoli and sweet pepper. Cook and stir for 1 to 2 minutes more or until vegetables are crisp-tender. Remove from wok.

4. Add beef strips to hot wok (Lightly coat skillet with nonstick cooking spray if needed). Cook and stir for 2 to 3 minutes or until meat is slightly pink in center. Push meat from center of wok.

5. Stir sauce. Add sauce to center of wok. Cook and stir until thickened and bubbly. Return cooked vegetables to wok; stir to coat all ingredients with sauce. Cook and stir for 1 to 2 minutes more or until heated through. Serve immediately with rice. If desired, sprinkle with sesame seeds. **MAKES 4 SERVINGS**

Beef Stroganoff

PREP: 30 minutes   SLOW COOK: 8 hours (low) or 4 hours (high) + 30 minutes (high)

NUTRITION FACTS PER SERVING

Calories 342   *Fat* 12 g   *Cholesterol* 89 mg   *Sodium* 441 mg   *Carbohydrates* 22 g   *Fiber* 1 g   *Protein* 32 g

1½ pounds beef stew meat
2   teaspoons vegetable oil
2   cups sliced fresh mushrooms
½   cup chopped onion,
     (1 medium)
2   cloves garlic, minced
½   teaspoon dried oregano,
     crushed
½   teaspoon salt
¼   teaspoon dried thyme,
     crushed
¼   teaspoon black pepper
1   bay leaf
1   14.5-ounce can lower-sodium
     beef broth
⅓   cup dry sherry or lower-
     sodium beef broth
1   8-ounce carton light sour
     cream
2   tablespoons cornstarch
2   cups hot cooked noodles
     Snipped fresh parsley
     (optional)

1. Trim fat from beef. Cut beef into 1-inch pieces. In a large skillet cook beef, half at a time, in hot oil over medium heat until browned. Drain off fat.

2. In a 3½- or 4-quart slow cooker place mushrooms, onion, garlic, oregano, salt, thyme, pepper, and bay leaf. Add beef. Pour broth and sherry over all in cooker.

3. Cover and cook on low-heat setting for 8 to 10 hours or on high-heat setting for 4 to 5 hours. Discard bay leaf.

4. If using low-heat setting, turn to high-heat setting. In a medium bowl combine sour cream and cornstarch. Gradually whisk about 1 cup of the hot cooking liquid into sour cream mixture; stir into cooker. Cover and cook about 30 minutes more or until thickened. Serve over hot cooked noodles. If desired, sprinkle each serving with parsley.
MAKES 6 SERVINGS

Herbed Steak with Balsamic Sauce

START TO FINISH: **20 minutes**

**NUTRITION FACTS
PER SERVING**

Calories 217
Fat 11 g
Cholesterol 75 mg
Sodium 281 mg
Carbohydrates 2 g
Fiber 0 g
Protein 25 g

1 teaspoon cracked black pepper
2 teaspoons dried Italian seasoning, crushed
1 teaspoon garlic powder
¼ teaspoon salt
2 boneless beef top loin steaks, cut ¾ inch thick
1 tablespoon olive oil
½ cup reduced-sodium beef broth
1 tablespoon balsamic vinegar
1 tablespoon butter
2 tablespoons snipped fresh parsley

1. In a small bowl combine cracked pepper, Italian seasoning, garlic powder, and salt. Sprinkle evenly over both sides of each steak; rub in with your fingers.

2. In a heavy large skillet heat oil over medium-low to medium heat. Add steaks; cook until desired doneness, turning once halfway through cooking time. Allow 10 to 13 minutes for medium-rare (145°F) to medium (160°F). Remove steaks from skillet, reserving drippings in the skillet. Keep steaks warm.

3. For sauce, carefully add beef broth and balsamic vinegar to the skillet; stir to scrape up any crusty browned bits from bottom of skillet. Bring to boiling. Boil gently, uncovered, about 4 minutes or until sauce is reduced by half. Remove from heat; stir in butter.

4. Divide sauce among 4 dinner plates. Cut each steak in half. Place a piece of meat on top of sauce on each plate; sprinkle with parsley. **MAKES 4 SERVINGS**

Cheesesteaks with Sweet Peppers and Mushrooms

PREP: 20 minutes
COOK: 12 minutes
BROIL: 2 minutes

NUTRITION FACTS PER SERVING

Calories 348
Fat 11 g
Cholesterol 45 mg
Sodium 562 mg
Carbohydrates 3 g
Fiber 2 g
Protein 28 g

4 teaspoons canola oil
1 pound boneless beef sirloin steak, trimmed and cut into thin strips
¼ teaspoon black pepper
⅛ teaspoon salt
1 portobello mushroom, stems and gills removed, cut into thin strips
1 yellow sweet pepper, cut into thin strips
1 poblano chile, seeded and cut into thin strips (see note, page 10)
1 onion, halved and thinly sliced
2 cloves garlic, minced
1 14- to 16-ounce loaf French bread
1 cup shredded reduced-fat Monterey Jack cheese (4 ounces)

1. In a very large nonstick skillet heat 2 teaspoons of the oil over medium-high heat. Add beef strips; sprinkle with black pepper and salt. Cook for 4 to 6 minutes or just until beef is slightly pink in the center, stirring frequently. Remove beef from skillet; cover and set aside.

2. In the same skillet combine the remaining 2 teaspoons oil, the mushroom strips, sweet pepper, poblano, onion, and garlic. Cook for 8 to 10 minutes or until vegetables are tender, stirring occasionally.

3. Meanwhile, preheat broiler. Split bread loaf in half horizontally. Scoop out the soft centers of the top and bottom of the loaf, leaving about a ½-inch shell. (Save soft bread centers for another use.) Place bread halves, cut sides up, on a large baking sheet.

4. Broil bread 5 to 6 inches from the heat for 1 to 2 minutes or until toasted. Spoon vegetable mixture into bottom half of the loaf. Top with steak strips and cheese. Remove loaf top from the baking sheet. Broil filled bottom half of loaf for 1 to 2 minutes or until cheese is melted. Place loaf top over filling. To serve, cut crosswise into 6 portions. **MAKES 6 SERVINGS**

Italian Shepherd's Pie

PREP: 25 minutes   CHILL: 4 hours   BAKE: 40 minutes   STAND: 5 minutes   OVEN: 375°F

NUTRITION FACTS PER SERVING

Calories 246   *Fat* 11 g   *Cholesterol* 47 mg   *Sodium* 338 mg   *Carbohydrates* 4 g   *Fiber* 2 g   *Protein* 16 g

¾ cup shredded pizza cheese or Italian cheese blend (3 ounces)
2 cups mashed potatoes* or refrigerated mashed potatoes
8 ounces lean ground beef
4 ounces bulk sweet Italian sausage
½ cup chopped onion (1 medium)
2 cups sliced zucchini or yellow summer squash
1 14.5-ounce can diced tomatoes, undrained
½ of a 6-ounce can tomato paste (⅓ cup)
¼ teaspoon black pepper
Paprika (optional)

1. Stir ½ cup of the cheese into the potatoes; set mixture aside.

2. In a large skillet cook ground beef, sausage, and onion until meat is brown and onion is tender. Drain off fat. Stir zucchini, undrained tomatoes, tomato paste, and pepper into meat mixture in skillet. Bring to boiling.

3. Divide meat mixture evenly among six 10-ounce individual casserole dishes. Spoon mashed potato mixture into mounds on top of hot meat mixture in casseroles. Sprinkle with remaining ¼ cup cheese. If desired, sprinkle with paprika. Cover with plastic wrap; chill for at least 4 hours or up to 48 hours.

4. To serve, preheat oven to 375°F. Remove plastic wrap; place casseroles in a 15×10×1-inch baking pan. Cover with foil. Bake for 35 minutes. Remove foil. Bake, uncovered, for 5 minutes more. Let stand for 5 minutes before serving. **MAKES 6 SERVINGS**

*Mashed potatoes: To make mashed potatoes, wash and peel 1 pound potatoes. Cut potatoes into quarters or cubes. In a covered medium saucepan cook potatoes in a small amount of boiling salted water for 20 to 25 minutes or until tender. Mash with a potato masher or beat with an electric mixer on low until lumps are gone.

Beefy Stuffed Shells

PREP: 30 minutes
BAKE: 25 minutes
OVEN: 350°F

NUTRITION FACTS
PER SERVING

Calories 310
Fat 9 g
Cholesterol 45 mg
Sodium 322 mg
Carbohydrates 3 g
Fiber 6 g
Protein 24 g

Nonstick cooking spray
12 dried jumbo shell macaroni
12 ounces 95% lean ground beef
1 tablespoon olive oil
1½ cups chopped fresh
mushrooms (4 ounces)
1 cup chopped onion (1 large)
½ cup shredded carrot
¼ cup chopped celery
4 cloves garlic, minced
½ teaspoon dried Italian
seasoning, crushed
1 14.5-ounce can no-salt-added
diced tomatoes with basil,
garlic, and oregano, undrained
¼ teaspoon salt
1 cup shredded reduced-fat
Italian cheese blend
(2 ounces)
½ cup seeded and chopped
tomato (1 medium)
1 tablespoon snipped fresh basil
(optional)

1. Preheat oven to 350°F. Lightly coat a 2-quart square baking dish with cooking spray; set aside. Cook pasta according to package directions; drain. Rinse with cold water; drain again. Set aside.

2. Meanwhile, in a medium skillet cook ground beef until browned, using a wooden spoon to break up meat as it cooks. Drain off fat. Set meat aside.

3. In a large nonstick skillet heat oil over medium heat. Add mushrooms, onion, carrot, celery, garlic, and Italian seasoning; cook for 6 to 8 minutes or until tender, stirring frequently. Add diced tomatoes and salt. Cook and stir for 2 minutes more. Remove from heat; cool slightly.

4. Spoon the tomato mixture into a blender or food processor; cover and blend or process until nearly smooth. Set aside ¾ cup of the pureed tomato mixture. Return the remaining pureed tomato mixture to the skillet. Stir cooked meat into tomato mixture in skillet. Spoon 1 rounded tablespoon of the meat mixture into each pasta shell.

5. Arrange filled pasta shells in prepared baking dish. Spoon the reserved ¾ cup pureed tomato mixture over the shells.

6. Cover and bake for 20 minutes. Sprinkle with cheese and fresh tomato. Bake about 5 minutes more or until heated through and cheese is melted. If desired, sprinkle with basil. MAKES 6 SERVINGS

Skillet Roasted Potatoes with Pork and Wilted Arugula

PREP: 45 minutes
ROAST: 25 minutes
STAND: 10 minutes
OVEN: 425°F

NUTRITION FACTS
PER SERVING

Calories 232
Fat 9 g
Cholesterol 55 mg
Sodium 352 mg
Carbohydrates 17 g
Fiber 3 g
Protein 21 g

1   teaspoon dried rosemary, crushed
¼   teaspoon salt
¼   teaspoon black pepper
1   12- to 16-ounce pork tenderloin
12 ounces 2- to 3-inch Yukon gold potatoes, quartered
2   tablespoons olive oil
2   cloves garlic, thinly sliced
1   teaspoon finely shredded lemon peel
¼   teaspoon salt
¼   teaspoon smoked paprika or regular paprika
8   cups arugula, tough stems removed, or fresh baby spinach (about 6 ounces)

1. Preheat oven to 425°F. In a small bowl combine rosemary, ¼ teaspoon salt, and the pepper. Trim fat from meat. Place meat on a rack in a shallow roasting pan. Sprinkle all over with the rosemary mixture. Roast, uncovered, for 20 to 30 minutes or until an instant-read thermometer inserted in center registers 145°F. Remove from oven. Cover with foil; let stand for at least 3 minutes.

2. Meanwhile, in a covered large nonstick skillet cook potatoes in a small amount of boiling lightly salted water about 15 minutes or just until potatoes are tender, stirring occasionally. Drain water from skillet.

3. Add 1 tablespoon of the oil and the garlic to potatoes in skillet. Cook over medium-high heat for 5 to 10 minutes or until potatoes are browned, stirring occasionally. Sprinkle with lemon peel, ¼ teaspoon salt, and the paprika. Toss to coat. Transfer potatoes to a bowl. Cover and keep warm.

4. In the same skillet heat the remaining 1 tablespoon oil over medium heat. Add arugula, in batches if necessary. Cook and toss for 30 to 60 seconds or just until arugula is wilted.

5. To serve, divide arugula among 4 serving plates. Top with potatoes. Thinly slice pork crosswise; arrange on plates.
MAKES 4 SERVINGS

Pork Skewers with Fruit Glaze

PREP: 30 minutes   GRILL: 10 minutes

NUTRITION FACTS PER SERVING

Calories 187   *Fat* 4 g   *Cholesterol* 85 mg   *Sodium* 268 mg   *Carbohydrates* 18 g   *Fiber* 1 g   *Protein* 19 g

1   egg lightly beaten
⅓   cup finely chopped water chestnuts
¼   cup fine dry bread crumbs
2   teaspoons grated fresh ginger
1   clove garlic, minced
¼   teaspoon salt
¼   teaspoon black pepper
1   pound lean ground pork loin
1   red, yellow, or green sweet pepper, cut into 1-inch pieces
1   recipe Fruit Glaze

1. In a large bowl combine egg, water chestnuts, bread crumbs, ginger, garlic, salt, and pepper. Add ground pork; mix well. Shape pork mixture into thirty 1¼- to 1½-inch meatballs.

2. On 6 long skewers* alternately thread meatballs and sweet pepper pieces, leaving a ¼-inch space between pieces.

3. For a charcoal grill, arrange medium-hot coals around a drip pan. Place skewers on well-greased grill rack over pan. Cover; grill for 10 to 12 minutes or until meatballs are no longer pink and juices run clear. Brush with some of the Fruit Glaze. Immediately remove skewers from grill. (For a gas grill, preheat grill. Reduce heat to medium. Adjust for indirect cooking. Grill as above.)

4. Serve skewers with remaining glaze. **MAKES 6 SERVINGS**

Fruit Glaze: Place ⅔ cup desired flavor low-sugar fruit preserves in a small saucepan; snip any large pieces. Stir in ¼ cup pineapple juice, 1 tablespoon lemon juice, and ¼ teaspoon ground cardamom. Bring to boiling; reduce heat. Simmer, uncovered, for 15 minutes. Cool about 10 minutes (glaze will thicken as it cools). Makes about ¾ cup.

*Note: If using wooden skewers, soak skewers in enough water to cover for at least 30 minutes before grilling.

Asian Pork Quesadillas

START TO FINISH: 30 minutes
OVEN: 300°F

NUTRITION FACTS PER SERVING

Calories 253
Fat 12 g
Cholesterol 37 mg
Sodium 463 mg
Carbohydrates 5 g
Fiber 10 g
Protein 19 g

8 ounces pork tenderloin, cut into thin bite-size strips
½ teaspoon ground ginger
½ teaspoon black pepper
2 to 3 teaspoons olive oil or canola oil
½ of a red onion, cut into thin wedges
3 cups shredded napa cabbage
4 8-inch low-carb whole whole wheat tortillas
Nonstick cooking spray
1 recipe Peanut Sauce
Shredded napa cabbage (optional)

1. In a medium bowl toss pork with ginger and pepper to coat. In a large nonstick skillet heat 2 teaspoons of the oil over medium-high heat. Add pork; stir-fry about 3 minutes or until pork is cooked through. Remove pork from skillet; cover to keep warm.

2. If needed, add remaining oil to skillet. Add onion; cook and stir for 2 minutes. Add the 3 cups cabbage; cook and stir 2 minutes more or just until onion is tender and cabbage starts to wilt. Stir pork into cabbage mixture in skillet.

3. To assemble, coat one side of each tortilla lightly with cooking spray. Place tortillas, coated sides down, on a work surface. Using a slotted spoon, spoon pork mixture on top side of each tortilla. Drizzle with Peanut Sauce. Fold tortilla over filling.

4. Preheat a large skillet over medium heat for 1 minute. Place 2 of the quesadillas in the hot skillet; cook for 4 to 6 minutes or until browned, turning once. Remove quesadillas from skillet; place on a baking sheet. Keep warm in a 300°F oven. Repeat to cook the remaining quesadillas. If desired, serve quesadillas with additional shredded cabbage.
MAKES 4 SERVINGS

Peanut Sauce: In a small saucepan whisk together ½ cup creamy peanut butter; ½ cup water; 2 tablespoons reduced-sodium soy sauce; 2 cloves garlic, minced; ½ teaspoon ground ginger; and ¼ teaspoon crushed red pepper. Heat over medium-low heat until mixture is smooth, whisking constantly. Makes about 1 cup.

Turkey Orzo with Dried Cherries and Feta Cheese

PREP: 15 minutes
SLOW COOK: 2 hours (low)

NUTRITION FACTS PER SERVING

Calories 334
Fat 5 g
Cholesterol 61 mg
Sodium 451 mg
Carbohydrates 1 g
Fiber 3 g
Protein 30 g

Nonstick cooking spray
1¾ cups whole wheat orzo
1½ pounds turkey breast, cut into ½-inch cubes
2¾ cups reduced-sodium chicken broth
1¼ cups red onion, cut into ¼-inch pieces
½ cup dried cherries
2 tablespoons lemon juice
3 cloves garlic, minced
½ teaspoon black pepper
¼ teaspoon salt
6 cups lightly packed baby spinach
½ cup feta cheese (2 ounces)
¼ cup chopped almonds
1 tablespoon snipped fresh parsley

1. Coat a large skillet with cooking spray. Heat over medium heat. Add orzo; cook and stir for 3 to 4 minutes or until golden.

2. Coat a 4-quart slow cooker with cooking spray. In cooker combine orzo, turkey, broth, onion, cherries, lemon juice, garlic, pepper, and salt.

3. Cover and cook on low-heat setting for 2 hours.

4. Serve mixture on top of spinach. Sprinkle with cheese, almonds, and parsley.
MAKES 8 SERVINGS

Smoked Turkey and Bulgur

PREP: 20 minutes   SLOW COOK: 3 hours (low)

NUTRITION FACTS PER SERVING

Calories 216   *Fat* 7 g   *Cholesterol* 57 mg   *Sodium* 684 mg   *Carbohydrates* 2 g   *Fiber* 4 g   *Protein* 22 g

Nonstick cooking spray
1   cup chopped onion
      (1 medium)
1   cup coarsely chopped green
      sweet pepper (1 medium)
½ cup sliced celery (1 stalk)
1½ cups water
1   medium smoked turkey
      drumstick, skin and bone
      removed, meat chopped
      (about 4 cups)
1   cup uncooked bulgur
¼ teaspoon black pepper
1½ cups coarsely chopped
      zucchini (1 medium)
1   tablespoon snipped fresh sage
      Whole sage leaf (optional)

1. Coat an unheated 4-quart slow cooker with cooking spray. Place onion, sweet pepper, and celery in the cooker. Stir in the water, turkey, bulgur, and black pepper.

2. Cover and cook on low-heat setting for 2½ hours. Stir in zucchini and snipped sage. Cover and cook for 30 minutes more. If desired, garnish with a sage leaf.

MAKES 8 SERVINGS

Grilled Turkey Gyros

PREP: 25 minutes
GRILL: 6 minutes

NUTRITION FACTS PER SERVING

Calories 332
Fat 9 g
Cholesterol 95 mg
Sodium 560 mg
Carbohydrates 4 g
Fiber 6 g
Protein 31 g

12 ounces uncooked ground turkey breast
¼ cup finely chopped onion
1 egg, lightly beaten
1 tablespoon fine dry bread crumbs
2 cloves garlic, minced
1 teaspoon ground coriander
½ teaspoon ground cumin
⅛ teaspoon salt
⅛ teaspoon black pepper
1 tablespoon olive oil
4 whole wheat pita bread rounds
1 cup thinly sliced cucumber
1 cup diced tomato (2 medium)
2 tablespoons snipped fresh parsley
1 recipe Cucumber-Yogurt Sauce

1. For patties, in a large bowl combine turkey breast, onion, egg, bread crumbs, garlic, coriander, cumin, salt, and pepper. Shape mixture into 12 patties, flattening each to about ½-inch thickness. Brush all sides of the patties with olive oil. Wrap pita bread rounds in foil.

2. For a charcoal grill, place patties and foil-wrapped pita bread on the greased grill rack directly over medium coals. Grill, uncovered, about 6 minutes or until an instant-read thermometer inserted into each patty registers 165°F and pitas are heated through, turning once halfway through grilling. (For a gas grill, preheat grill; reduce heat to medium. Place patties and foil-wrapped pita bread on grill rack directly over heat. Cover and grill as above.)

3. Divide cucumber slices among grilled pita bread rounds. Top each with 3 patties, ¼ cup tomato, and some of the parsley. Drizzle with Cucumber-Yogurt Sauce. Fold pitas around fillings; secure with toothpicks. **MAKES 4 SERVINGS**

Cucumber-Yogurt Sauce:
In a small bowl combine ⅓ cup plain fat-free yogurt; ¼ cup shredded, seeded cucumber; 1 tablespoon tahini (sesame seed paste); 2 cloves garlic, minced; and ⅛ teaspoon salt. Cover and chill for at least 20 minutes.

Orange-Balsamic Marinated Shrimp

PREP: 20 minutes
MARINATE: 1 hour
BROIL: 4 minutes

NUTRITION FACTS PER SERVING

Calories 114
Fat 3 g
Cholesterol 129 mg
Sodium 181 mg
Carbohydrates 1 g
Fiber 0 g
Protein 17 g

1   pound fresh or frozen extra-large shrimp in shells
2   tablespoons white balsamic vinegar
½   teaspoon finely shredded orange peel
2   tablespoons orange juice
2   tablespoons finely chopped shallot or onion
1   tablespoon olive oil
¼   teaspoon salt
    Finely shredded orange peel

1. Thaw shrimp, if frozen. Peel and devein shrimp, leaving tails intact if desired. Rinse shrimp and pat dry with paper towels. Place shrimp in a large resealable plastic bag set in a shallow bowl.

2. In a small bowl combine vinegar, ½ teaspoon orange peel, orange juice, shallot, olive oil, and salt. Pour over shrimp. Seal bag and toss gently to coat shrimp. Marinate in the refrigerator for 1 to 4 hours.

3. Preheat broiler. Remove shrimp from marinade, discarding marinade. Arrange shrimp on the unheated rack of a broiler pan. Broil 4 to 5 inches from the heat for 4 to 6 minutes or until shrimp are opaque, turning once halfway through broiling. Sprinkle shrimp with additional orange peel.
MAKES 4 SERVINGS

Asian Sesame Noodles
with Shrimp

START TO FINISH: 30 minutes

NUTRITION FACTS PER SERVING

Calories 285   *Fat* 7 g   *Cholesterol* 86 mg   *Sodium* 284 mg   *Carbohydrates* 35 g   *Fiber* 4 g   *Protein* 19 g

8 ounces fresh or frozen shrimp, peeled and deveined
6 ounces udon noodles
1 cup snow peas, trimmed and halved diagonally
⅔ cup carrots, julienned
½ cup bok choy, thinly sliced
2 tablespoons rice vinegar
1 tablespoon canola oil
2 teaspoons grated fresh ginger
1 teaspoon reduced-sodium soy sauce
1 teaspoon toasted sesame oil
1 clove garlic, minced
½ teaspoon honey
¼ teaspoon crushed red pepper
⅛ teaspoon salt
1 teaspoon sesame seeds, toasted (see note, page 46)

1. Thaw shrimp, if frozen. Cook noodles according to package directions, adding shrimp and snow peas during the last 3 minutes of cooking time; drain. Rinse under cold running water to stop cooking; drain again.

2. In a serving bowl combine noodle mixture, carrots, and bok choy. In a screw-top jar combine rice vinegar, canola oil, ginger, soy sauce, sesame oil, garlic, honey, crushed red pepper, and salt. Pour mixture over noodle mixture and toss to coat. Sprinkle with sesame seeds. Cover and chill until ready to serve or up to 2 hours.
MAKES 4 SERVINGS

Coconut Shrimp with Mango Rice Pilaf

PREP: 25 minutes
BAKE: 8 minutes
OVEN: 450°F

NUTRITION FACTS PER SERVING

Calories 328
Fat 8 g
Cholesterol 172 mg
Sodium 291 mg
Carbohydrates 35 g
Fiber 3 g
Protein 29 g

1 pound fresh or frozen extra-large shrimp in shells
Nonstick cooking spray
¼ cup refrigerated or frozen egg product, thawed, or 2 egg whites, lightly beaten
¾ cup finely crushed reduced-fat or reduced-sodium shredded wheat crackers
⅓ cup shredded coconut
¼ teaspoon ground ginger
¼ teaspoon black pepper
1 8.8-ounce package cooked brown rice
⅓ cup chopped fresh mango or chopped jarred mango, rinsed and drained
⅓ cup sliced green onions (3)
2 tablespoons snipped fresh cilantro

1. Thaw shrimp, if frozen. Preheat oven to 450°F. Lightly coat a large baking sheet with nonstick cooking spray; set aside. Peel and devein shrimp, leaving tails intact. Rinse shrimp; pat dry with paper towels.

2. Place egg in a shallow dish. In another shallow dish combine crushed crackers, coconut, ginger, and pepper. Dip shrimp into egg, turning to coat. Dip in coconut mixture, pressing to coat but leaving tails uncoated. Arrange shrimp in a single layer on the prepared baking sheet.

3. Bake for 8 to 10 minutes or until shrimp are opaque and coating is lightly browned. Meanwhile, heat rice according to package directions. Transfer to a serving bowl. Stir in mango and green onions. Serve rice with shrimp; sprinkle with cilantro.
MAKES 4 SERVINGS

CHAPTER 9

Soups

Creamy Chicken Noodle Soup

PREP: 25 minutes
SLOW COOK: 6 hours (low) or 3 hours (high) + 20 minutes (high)

NUTRITION FACTS PER SERVING

Calories 170
Fat 6 g
Cholesterol 54 mg
Sodium 401 mg
Carbohydrates 11 g
Fiber 2 g
Protein 17 g

1   32-ounce container reduced-sodium chicken broth
3   cups water
2½ cups chopped cooked chicken (about 12 ounces)
1½ cups carrots, sliced (3 medium)
1½ cups sliced celery (3 stalks)
1½ cups sliced fresh mushrooms (4 ounces)
¼   cup chopped onion
1½ teaspoons dried thyme, crushed
¾   teaspoon garlic-pepper seasoning
3   ounces reduced-fat cream cheese (Neufchâtel), cut up
2   cups dried egg noodles

1. In a 5- to 6-quart slow cooker combine broth, the water, chicken, carrots, celery, mushrooms, onion, thyme, and garlic-pepper seasoning.

2. Cover and cook on low-heat setting for 6 to 8 hours or on high-heat setting for 3 to 4 hours.

3. If using low-heat setting, turn to high-heat setting. Stir in cream cheese until combined. Stir in uncooked noodles. Cover and cook for 20 to 30 minutes more or just until noodles are tender.
MAKES 8 SERVINGS

CHAPTER 10

Sides

Gingered Lemon Broccoli Salad

PREP: 20 minutes
CHILL: 1 hour

NUTRITION FACTS PER SERVING

Calories 59
Fat 3 g
Cholesterol 2 mg
Sodium 54 mg
Carbohydrates 8 g
Fiber 2 g
Protein 2 g

3 tablespoons light mayonnaise
  or salad dressing
2 tablespoons plain soy yogurt
¼ teaspoon finely shredded
  lemon peel
2 teaspoons lemon juice
¼ teaspoon grated fresh ginger
4 cups small broccoli and/or
  cauliflower florets
⅓ cup finely chopped red onion
¼ cup dried cranberries
3 tablespoons roasted soy nuts

1. In a large bowl stir together mayonnaise, soy yogurt, lemon peel, lemon juice, and ginger. Add broccoli, red onion, and cranberries. Toss to coat. Cover and chill for 1 to 24 hours. Just before serving, sprinkle with soy nuts. **MAKES 8 SERVINGS**

Farmer's Market Salad Platter

PREP: 25 minutes
COOK: 20 minutes

NUTRITION FACTS PER SERVING

Calories 106
Fat 4 g
Cholesterol 0 mg
Sodium 49 mg
Carbohydrates 3 g
Fiber 3 g
Protein 3 g

1¼ pounds tiny new potatoes, halved or quartered

12 ounces fresh green beans and/or yellow wax beans, trimmed

¼ cup white wine vinegar or champagne vinegar

3 tablespoons olive oil

1 shallot, finely chopped (2 tablespoons)

1 tablespoon capers, rinsed and drained

1 teaspoon Dijon mustard

¼ teaspoon freshly ground black pepper

5 cups fresh baby arugula or baby spinach

4 roma tomatoes, coarsely chopped

1. In a covered large saucepan cook potatoes in enough boiling water to cover about 10 minutes or just until tender; drain. Rinse with cold water and drain again. If desired, cover and chill for up to 24 hours.

2. In a covered medium saucepan cook beans in enough boiling water to cover about 10 minutes or just until crisp-tender; drain. Submerse beans in a bowl of ice water to cool quickly; drain again. If desired, cover and chill for up to 24 hours.

3. For dressing, in a screw-top jar combine vinegar, olive oil, shallot, capers, mustard, and pepper. Cover and shake well. If desired, chill for up to 24 hours.

4. To serve, if dressing is chilled, let it stand at room temperature for 30 minutes. Arrange arugula on a platter. Arrange potatoes, beans, and tomatoes on top of arugula. Shake the dressing well. Drizzle dressing over vegetables.
MAKES 10 SERVINGS

Green Apple Slaw

PREP: 30 minutes   CHILL: 1 hour

NUTRITION FACTS PER SERVING

Calories 67   *Fat* 3 g   *Cholesterol* 4 mg   *Sodium* 73 mg   *Carbohydrates* 10 g   *Fiber* 1 g   *Protein* 0 g

½ cup light mayonnaise or salad dressing
2 teaspoons honey
½ teaspoon poppy seeds
4 Granny Smith apples, quartered and thinly sliced (4 cups)
1 tablespoon lemon juice
1½ cups coarsely chopped cabbage
¾ cup halved green seedless grapes
½ cup thinly sliced celery

1. For dressing, in a small bowl stir together mayonnaise, honey, and poppy seeds. Set aside.

2. In a large salad bowl combine apples and lemon juice; toss to combine. Stir in cabbage, grapes, and celery. Pour dressing over mixture; toss gently to coat. Cover and chill in the refrigerator for 1 to 24 hours before serving.

MAKES 12 SERVINGS

Crunchy Zucchini and Tomato

START TO FINISH: 15 minutes

NUTRITION FACTS PER SERVING

Calories 54
Fat 2 g
Cholesterol 4 mg
Sodium 105 mg
Carbohydrates 7 g
Fiber 1 g
Protein 3 g

1 medium zucchini, trimmed and cut lengthwise into 4 slices
   Nonstick cooking spray
1 large tomato, cut into 4 slices
¼ teaspoon dried Italian seasoning, crushed
¼ teaspoon black pepper
⅓ cup panko (Japanese-style bread crumbs)
¼ cup finely shredded Parmesan cheese (1 ounce)
1 clove garlic, minced

1. Preheat broiler. Coat both sides of zucchini slices with cooking spray. Sprinkle zucchini and tomato slices with Italian seasoning and pepper.

2. Place zucchini slices on the unheated rack of a broiler pan. Broil 4 to 5 inches from the heat about 8 minutes or until crisp-tender, turning once halfway through broiling.

3. Meanwhile, in a small bowl combine bread crumbs, cheese, and garlic. Place tomato slices on broiler pan next to zucchini slices. Sprinkle tops of vegetable slices with bread crumb mixture. Broil for 1 to 2 minutes more or until topping is golden. **MAKES 4 SERVINGS**

Lemon-Dill Cauliflower and Broccoli

PREP: 25 minutes
GRILL: 20 minutes

NUTRITION FACTS
PER SERVING

Calories 60
Fat 4 g
Cholesterol 0 mg
Sodium 103 mg
Carbohydrates 6 g
Fiber 2 g
Protein 2 g

2   cups cauliflower florets
2   cups broccoli florets
1   tablespoon olive oil
2   teaspoons snipped fresh
    dillweed or ½ teaspoon dried
    dillweed
¼   teaspoon finely shredded
    lemon peel
2   teaspoons lemon juice
1   small clove garlic, minced
⅛   teaspoon salt
⅛   teaspoon dry mustard
⅛   teaspoon black pepper
    Fresh dill sprigs (optional)

1. Fold a 36×18-inch piece of heavy-duty foil in half to make an 18-inch square. Place cauliflower and broccoli in center of the foil square.

2. In a small bowl combine oil, dill, lemon peel, lemon juice, garlic, salt, mustard, and pepper; drizzle over vegetables. Bring up two opposite edges of the foil and seal with a double fold. Fold remaining ends to completely enclose the food, allowing space for steam to build.

3. For a charcoal grill, place foil packet on the grill rack directly over medium coals. Grill, uncovered, about 20 minutes or until vegetables are tender, turning packet once halfway through cooking and carefully opening packet to check doneness. (For a gas grill, preheat grill. Reduce heat to medium. Place foil packet on grill rack over heat. Cover and grill as above.) Remove from foil packet. If desired, garnish with fresh dill sprigs. **MAKES 4 SERVINGS**

Oven Method: Preheat oven to 350°F. Prepare as directed through Step 2. Bake packet directly on the oven rack about 35 minutes or until vegetables are tender, turning packet once halfway through cooking and carefully opening packet to check doneness.

Greek Garden Pasta Salad

PREP: 35 minutes   CHILL: 3 hours

NUTRITION FACTS PER SERVING

Calories 98   *Fat* 3 g   *Cholesterol* 3 mg   *Sodium* 100 mg   *Carbohydrates* 1 g   *Fiber* 2 g   *Protein* 3 g

6   ounces dried whole grain or multigrain bow tie or rotini pasta (2⅔ cups)
1   6-ounce carton regular plain fat-free yogurt or Greek plain fat-free yogurt (⅔ cup)
⅓   cup light mayonnaise or salad dressing
2   tablespoons fat-free milk
2   tablespoons snipped fresh dill or 1½ teaspoons dried dill
2   tablespoons snipped fresh parsley
1   teaspoon finely shredded lemon peel
1   tablespoon lemon juice
½   teaspoon freshly ground black pepper
1½ cups chopped English cucumber (1)
1½ cups halved grape tomatoes
¾   cup chopped green sweet pepper
⅓   cup sliced green onions (3)
⅓   cup quartered pitted kalamata olives

1. Cook pasta according to package directions. Drain well. Rinse with cold water and drain again.

2. For dressing, in a large bowl stir together yogurt, mayonnaise, milk, dill, parsley, lemon peel and juice, and pepper.

3. Stir the pasta, cucumber, tomatoes, sweet pepper, and green onions into the dressing. Toss gently to coat. Cover and chill in the refrigerator for 3 to 6 hours before serving. To serve, fold in kalamata olives. **MAKES 12 SERVINGS**

Caribbean Couscous Salad

PREP: 20 minutes
COOL: 10 minutes
STAND: 5 minutes

NUTRITION FACTS PER SERVING

Calories 140
Fat 3 g
Cholesterol 0 mg
Sodium 142 mg
Carbohydrates 25 g
Fiber 5 g
Protein 6 g

1¼ cups water
1   cup whole wheat couscous
1   15-ounce can black beans or kidney beans, rinsed and drained
2   cups coarsely shredded fresh spinach
¾   cup coarsely chopped red sweet pepper
1   mango, peeled, seeded, and chopped
2   green onions, thinly sliced (2)
1   recipe Ginger-Lime Vinaigrette

1. In a medium saucepan bring the water to boiling. Remove from heat. Stir in couscous; cover and let stand for 5 minutes. Fluff with a fork. Let stand at room temperature about 10 minutes or until cool.

2. In a large bowl stir together beans, spinach, sweet pepper, mango, and green onions. Add couscous and Ginger-Lime Vinaigrette. Toss to coat. Serve immediately or cover and chill in the refrigerator for up to 24 hours.
MAKES 10 SERVINGS

Ginger-Lime Vinaigrette: In a bowl whisk together ¼ cup snipped fresh cilantro, 3 tablespoons lime juice, 2 tablespoons canola oil, 1½ teaspoons grated fresh ginger or ½ teaspoon ground ginger, ⅛ teaspoon salt, and ⅛ teaspoon cayenne pepper.

Smoky Baked Beans

PREP: 20 minutes
COOK: 10 minutes
BAKE: 1 hour
OVEN: 375°F

NUTRITION FACTS PER SERVING

Calories 218
Fat 6 g
Cholesterol 9 mg
Sodium 168 mg
Carbohydrates 31 g
Fiber 10 g
Protein 11 g

6   slices bacon, chopped
¾   cup chopped green sweet pepper (1 medium)
½   cup chopped onion (1 medium)
2   cloves garlic, minced
1   15-ounce can no-salt-added black beans, rinsed and drained
1   15-ounce can no-salt-added butter beans or cannellini beans, rinsed and drained
1   15-ounce can no-salt-added red kidney beans, rinsed and drained
1   8-ounce can no-salt-added tomato sauce
¼   cup orange juice
2   tablespoons packed brown sugar
1   tablespoon Worcestershire sauce
1   fresh jalapeño pepper, seeded and finely chopped (see note, page 10)
    Crisp-cooked bacon, crumbled (optional)
    Fresh jalapeño pepper, sliced (see note, page 10) (optional)

1. Preheat oven to 375°F. In a large skillet cook chopped bacon, sweet pepper, onion, and garlic over medium heat about 10 minutes or until bacon is crisp and onion is tender; drain.

2. In a large bowl combine bacon mixture, black beans, butter beans, kidney beans, tomato sauce, orange juice, brown sugar, Worcestershire sauce, and jalapeño. Spoon mixture into a 1½-quart casserole.

3. Bake, covered, for 1 hour, stirring once halfway through baking. If desired, garnish with crumbled bacon and additional sliced jalapeño. **MAKES 8 SERVINGS**

Moroccan-Style Simmered Beans

PREP: 15 minutes
COOK: 30 minutes

NUTRITION FACTS PER SERVING

Calories 127
Fat 2 g
Cholesterol 0 mg
Sodium 202 mg
Carbohydrates 1 g
Fiber 6 g
Protein 8 g

2 teaspoons canola oil
½ cup chopped sweet onion
½ cup chopped carrot
   (1 medium)
1 clove garlic, minced
¼ teaspoon ground cumin
¼ teaspoon ground coriander
⅛ teaspoon crushed red pepper
⅛ teaspoon ground cinnamon
1 15-ounce can garbanzo beans
   (chickpeas), rinsed and
   drained
1 15-ounce can Great Northern
   beans, rinsed and drained
½ cup frozen baby lima beans
½ cup chopped tomatoes
⅓ cup water
1 tablespoon lemon juice
   Ground cumin and/or crushed
   red pepper (optional)

1. In a large saucepan heat oil. Add onion and carrot to skillet; cook over medium heat for 8 to 10 minutes or until very tender, stirring occasionally. Stir in garlic, ¼ teaspoon cumin, the coriander, ⅛ teaspoon crushed red pepper, and the cinnamon. Cook and stir for 1 minute.

2. Add beans, tomatoes, and the water. Bring to boiling; reduce heat. Cover and cook for 20 minutes to blend flavors, stirring occasionally. Stir in lemon juice just before serving. If desired, sprinkle with additional cumin and/or crushed red pepper.
MAKES 8 SERVINGS

CHAPTER 11

Desserts

Apple-Spice Cake

PREP: 25 minutes
BAKE: 35 minutes
OVEN: 350°F

NUTRITION FACTS PER SERVING

Calories 193
Fat 7 g
Cholesterol 25 mg
Sodium 186 mg
Carbohydrates 1 g
Fiber 2 g
Protein 4 g

Nonstick cooking spray
¾ cup all-purpose flour
½ cup white whole wheat flour
¼ cup flaxseed meal
1 teaspoon baking powder
¾ teaspoon ground cinnamon
½ teaspoon baking soda
½ teaspoon ground ginger
¼ teaspoon salt
⅛ teaspoon ground cloves
1 egg, lightly beaten
1 6-ounce carton plain low-fat yogurt
⅓ cup packed brown sugar
¼ cup unsweetened applesauce
3 tablespoons vegetable oil
1 tablespoon molasses
1 apple (such as Granny Smith, Braeburn, or Gala), cored and finely chopped (1 cup)
⅔ cup frozen light whipped dessert topping, thawed
  Ground cinnamon

1. Preheat oven to 350°F. Lightly coat an 8×8×2-inch baking pan with cooking spray; set aside.

2. In a large bowl stir together all-purpose flour, white whole wheat flour, flaxseed meal, baking powder, cinnamon, baking soda, ginger, salt, and cloves. In a medium bowl combine egg, yogurt, brown sugar, applesauce, oil, and molasses. Add egg mixture to flour mixture; stir just until combined. Fold in apple. Spread batter evenly in the prepared baking pan.

3. Bake about 35 minutes or until a toothpick inserted near center comes out clean. Cool slightly on a wire rack.

4. To serve, cut cake into 9 squares. Serve warm. Top each serving with whipped topping and sprinkle with additional cinnamon.
MAKES 9 SERVINGS

May Basket Cupcakes

PREP: 40 minutes
BAKE: 18 minutes
OVEN: 350°F

NUTRITION FACTS PER SERVING

Calories 186
Fat 6 g
Cholesterol 14 mg
Sodium 157 mg
Carbohydrates 30 g
Fiber 1 g
Protein 3 g

Nonstick cooking spray
1⅔ cups all-purpose flour
1½ teaspoons finely shredded lime peel
1¼ teaspoons baking powder
½ teaspoon baking soda
⅛ teaspoon salt
¼ cup butter, softened
¾ cup sugar
½ cup refrigerated or frozen egg product, thawed, or 2 eggs
⅔ cup light sour cream
2 tablespoons fat-free milk
1½ cups sliced or coarsely chopped fresh strawberries, kiwifruit, pineapple, and/or whole fresh raspberries or blueberries
1 cup frozen light whipped dessert topping, thawed
2 tablespoons coconut chips, lightly toasted (see note, page 46) (optional)

1. Preheat oven to 350°F. Line twelve 2½-inch muffin cups with paper bake cups. Coat paper bake cups with cooking spray; set aside. In a medium bowl combine flour, lime peel, baking powder, baking soda, and salt; set aside.

2. In a large bowl beat butter with an electric mixer on medium for 30 seconds. Gradually add sugar, beating until light and fluffy. Beat in eggs. In a small bowl combine sour cream and milk. Alternately add flour mixture and sour cream mixture to egg mixture, beating on low after each addition just until combined.

3. Spoon batter evenly into prepared muffin cups, filling each two-thirds to three-fourths full. Bake for 18 to 20 minutes or until a toothpick inserted near the centers comes out clean. Cool in cups on a wire rack for 5 minutes. Remove cupcakes from pans. Cool completely on wire rack.

4. Using a small knife, cut a shallow dip in the top of each cupcake. Save cut-off cake tops for another use, such as for making fruit parfaits. Top cupcakes with fruit, whipped topping, and, if desired, coconut. **MAKES 12 SERVINGS**

Plum Galettes

PREP: 30 minutes   BAKE: 30 minutes   OVEN: 375°F

NUTRITION FACTS PER SERVING

Calories 187   *Fat* 8 g   *Cholesterol* 11 mg   *Sodium* 136 mg   *Carbohydrates* 26 g   *Fiber* 1 g   *Protein* 4 g

2   ounces low-fat whipped tub-style cream cheese
2   tablespoons refrigerated or frozen egg product, or 1 egg yolk
2   tablespoons low-sugar orange marmalade
½   teaspoon ground ginger
1   recipe Browned Butter Pastry
4   plums, pitted and sliced ¼ inch thick
2   tablespoons almonds or walnuts, chopped
    Fat-free milk
4   teaspoons honey

1. Preheat oven to 375°F. Line a baking sheet with parchment paper; set aside. In a medium bowl beat cream cheese with an electric mixer on medium to high. Beat in egg product, orange marmalade, and ginger.

2. Prepare Browned Butter Pastry. Divide pastry dough into 4 portions. On a lightly floured surface roll dough portions to a 7-inch circle. Top each portion with some of the cream cheese mixture, leaving a 1-inch border. Top with plum slices and almonds. Fold border up over filling, pleating pastry as necessary to fit. Place galettes on baking sheet. Brush tops and sides of crust with milk.

3. Bake for 30 minutes or until crust is golden brown. Serve warm or cool. Drizzle with honey.
MAKES 8 SERVINGS

Browned Butter Pastry: In a small saucepan heat and stir 2 tablespoons butter over medium heat until light brown; set aside to cool slightly. In a medium bowl stir together 1¼ cups all-purpose flour, 1 tablespoon granulated sugar, and ¼ teaspoon salt. Using a pastry blender, cut in 2 tablespoons shortening and the browned butter until mixture resembles crumbs. Sprinkle 1 tablespoon cold water over part of the mixture; toss gently with a fork. Push moistened dough to side of bowl. Repeat moistening flour mixture, using 1 tablespoon cold water at a time, until all of the flour mixture is moistened (2 to 3 tablespoons total). Form dough into a ball.

Lemon Tart with Ginger-Oat Crust

PREP: 45 minutes
BAKE: 13 minutes
STAND: 15 minutes
CHILL: 1 hour
OVEN: 350°F

NUTRITION FACTS PER SERVING

Calories 186
Fat 9 g
Cholesterol 48 mg
Sodium 101 mg
Carbohydrates 25 g
Fiber 1 g
Protein 2 g

Nonstick cooking spray
1 recipe Ginger-Oat Crust
2 egg yolks or ¼ cup refrigerated or frozen egg product, thawed
⅔ cup sugar
2 tablespoons cornstarch
1 tablespoon finely shredded lemon peel
6 tablespoons lemon juice
6 tablespoons water
¼ cup tub-style 60% to 70% vegetable oil spread
½ cup light sour cream
   Lemon slices, lime slices, and/ or orange slices (optional)

1. Preheat oven to 350°F. Coat a 9-inch tart pan with removable bottom with cooking spray. Using your damp fingers press Ginger-Oat Crust dough onto bottom and up the side of the prepared tart pan. Line crust with a double thickness of foil that has been lightly coated on the bottom with cooking spray. Bake for 8 minutes. Carefully remove foil. Bake for 5 to 7 minutes more or until crust is lightly browned. Cool completely on a wire rack.

2. In a small bowl use a fork to lightly beat egg yolks; set aside. In a medium saucepan stir together sugar and cornstarch. Stir in lemon peel, lemon juice, and the water. Cook and stir over medium heat until thickened and bubbly. Stir half of the lemon mixture into egg yolks. Add egg mixture to lemon mixture in saucepan. Cook and stir over medium heat until mixture comes to a gentle

boil. Cook and stir for 2 minutes more. Remove from heat. Whisk in vegetable oil spread until well mixed. Cover surface of the cooked lemon mixture with plastic wrap. Let stand at room temperature for 15 minutes. Whisk in sour cream until well mixed.

3. Pour lemon mixture into cooled tart crust. Cover loosely and chill at least 1 hour before serving. Remove side of pan to serve. If desired, top with lemon, lime, and/ or orange slices. **MAKES 12 SERVINGS**

Ginger-Oat Crust: In a medium bowl beat ¼ cup softened butter with an electric mixer on medium for 3 seconds. Add 2 tablespoons packed brown sugar; beat until combined. Beat in 1 egg white and ½ teaspoon vanilla until combined. Beat in ⅓ cup all-purpose flour. Stir in ½ cup ground gingersnaps, ½ cup quick-cooking rolled oats, and ⅛ teaspoon ground ginger.

Vanilla Meringue Tarts

PREP: 40 minutes
BAKE: 1 hour 15 minutes
CHILL: 2 hours
OVEN: 250°F

1 recipe Meringue Shells
⅓ cup granulated sugar
2 tablespoons cornstarch
2¼ cups low-fat milk
¼ cup refrigerated or frozen egg product, thawed
1 tablespoon tub-style 60% to 70% vegetable oil spread
1½ teaspoons vanilla
1 cup fresh whole or sliced berries, sliced banana, sliced kiwifruit, sliced kumquats, and/or sliced oranges

1. Prepare Meringue Shells.

2. Meanwhile, for filling, combine sugar and cornstarch in a medium saucepan. Gradually stir in milk. Cook and stir over medium heat until thickened and bubbly; reduce heat. Cook and stir for 2 minutes more. Remove from heat. Gradually stir about 1 cup of the hot filling into egg. Add egg mixture to milk mixture in saucepan. Bring to a gentle boil; reduce heat. Cook and stir for 2 minutes more. Remove from heat. Stir in vegetable oil spread and vanilla. Place saucepan in a very large bowl half-filled with ice water. Stir filling constantly for 2 minutes to cool quickly. Transfer filling to a medium bowl. Cover surface of filling with plastic wrap. Chill for 2 to 24 hours.

3. Spoon filling into Meringue Shells. Serve at once or cover and chill for up to 30 minutes before serving. Top individual servings with fruit. **MAKES 10 SERVINGS**

Meringue Shells: Preheat oven to 250°F. Cover two large baking sheets with parchment paper. Draw ten 2½-inch circles on the paper. Set aside. In a medium bowl combine 2 egg whites, ½ teaspoon vanilla, ¼ teaspoon cream of tartar, and ⅛ teaspoon salt. Beat with an electric mixer on medium until soft peaks form (tips curl). Gradually add ½ cup sugar, about 1 tablespoon at a time, beating on high until stiff peaks form (tips stand straight). Spoon mixture into a pastry bag fitted with an open star tip. Pipe mixture in a spiral pattern over the circles on paper, piping the side of each circle up to a height of 1¼ inches. Bake about 1¼ hours or until meringues appear dry and are firm when lightly touched. Cool meringues on paper on wire rack. Peel from paper; transfer to a serving platter.

Lemon-Berry Pudding Cake

PREP: 20 minutes   STAND: : 30 minutes   SLOW COOK: 2½ hours (high)   COOL: 1 hour

NUTRITION FACTS PER SERVING

Calories 200   *Fat* 7 g   *Cholesterol* 107 mg   *Sodium* 187 mg   *Carbohydrates* 29 g   *Fiber* 1 g   *Protein* 5 g

3   eggs
    Nonstick cooking spray
1   cup fresh blueberries and/or
    fresh red raspberries
1   tablespoon granulated sugar
½   cup granulated sugar
¼   cup all-purpose flour
2   teaspoons finely shredded
    lemon peel
¼   teaspoon salt
1   cup fat-free milk
3   tablespoons lemon juice
3   tablespoons tub-style 60% to
    70% vegetable oil spread
    Powdered sugar (optional)

1. Let eggs stand at room temperature for 30 minutes. Meanwhile, coat a 2-quart slow cooker with cooking spray. Place berries in cooker and sprinkle with the 1 tablespoon granulated sugar.

2. For batter, separate eggs. In a medium bowl combine the ½ cup granulated sugar, the flour, lemon peel, and salt. Add milk, lemon juice, vegetable oil spread, and egg yolks. Beat with an electric mixer on low until combined. Beat on medium for 1 minute.

3. Thoroughly wash beaters. In another bowl beat egg whites with an electric mixer on medium until soft peaks form (tips curl). Fold egg whites into batter. Carefully pour batter over berries in cooker, spreading evenly.

4. Cover and cook on high-heat setting for 2½ to 3 hours. If cake begins to look too brown on one side, rotate the crockery liner 180° halfway through cooking. Turn off cooker. If possible remove crockery liner from cooker; cool, uncovered, for 1 hour on a wire rack before serving.

5. If desired, sprinkle with powdered sugar. **MAKES 6 SERVINGS**

Grilled Plum and Strawberry Kabobs with Sweet Mint Pesto

PREP: 20 minutes
GRILL: 3 minutes

NUTRITION FACTS PER SERVING

Calories 85
Fat 4 g
Cholesterol 0 mg
Sodium 36 mg
Carbohydrates 2 g
Fiber 1 g
Protein 3 g

⅔ cup lightly packed fresh mint leaves
¼ cup lightly packed fresh basil
3 tablespoons pine nuts, toasted (see note, page 46)
½ teaspoon finely shredded orange peel
3 tablespoons orange juice
   Dash salt
4 plums, pitted and cut into sixths
8 strawberries
   Nonstick cooking spray

1. In a blender or small food processor combine mint, basil, pine nuts, orange peel, orange juice, and salt. Cover and blend or process until smooth, stopping and scraping sides, as needed. Set aside.

2. Thread plum wedges and strawberries on eight 6-inch-long skewers (see note, page 122). Lightly coat fruit with cooking spray. For a charcoal grill, grill kabobs on the rack of an uncovered grill directly over medium coals for 3 to 4 minutes or until heated through and grill marks are visible, turning occasionally to brown evenly. (For a gas grill, preheat grill. Reduce heat to medium. Place kabobs on grill rack over heat. Cover and grill as directed.)

3. Serve kabobs with pesto.
MAKES 4 SERVINGS

Tiramisu Shots

PREP: 25 minutes
CHILL: 30 minutes

NUTRITION FACTS
PER SERVING

Calories 75
Fat 2 g
Cholesterol 0 mg
Sodium 106 mg
Carbohydrates 12 g
Fiber 0 g
Protein 3 g

1   ounce dark or bittersweet
    chocolate, chopped
1   12.3-ounce package firm
    silken tofu
¼   cup brewed espresso, cooled
¼   cup sugar
1   teaspoon lemon juice
⅛   teaspoon salt
24 1½- to 2-inch pieces
    purchased angel food cake
    (about ½ of a 7-inch cake)
2   tablespoons brewed espresso,
    cooled, or coffee-flavor liqueur
    Unsweetened cocoa powder
12 chocolate-covered espresso
    beans

1. Place chocolate in a food processor. Cover and process until finely chopped. Add tofu, ¼ cup espresso, sugar, lemon juice, and salt. Cover and process until nearly smooth.

2. Place a cake piece in the bottom of each of 12 shot glasses or demitasse cups, pressing lightly. Drizzle each with about ½ teaspoon espresso or liqueur. Spoon about 1 tablespoon of the tofu mixture over each cake piece in the glasses. Top each with remaining cake pieces. Spoon remaining tofu mixture over each.

3. Place glasses on a tray. Cover with plastic wrap. Chill for 30 minutes or up to 24 hours.

4. To serve, lightly sift cocoa powder over mixture in glasses and top each with an espresso bean.
MAKES 12 SERVINGS

Apple Spice Bars

PREP: 25 minutes   BAKE: 50 minutes   OVEN: 350°F

NUTRITION FACTS PER SERVING

Calories 167   Fat 4 g   Cholesterol 0 mg   Sodium 100 mg   Carbohydrates 30 g   Fiber 2 g   Protein 2 g

1½ cups all-purpose flour
½   cup quick cooking oats
⅓   cup granulated sugar
½   teaspoon baking powder
¼   teaspoon salt
½   cup 60% or more vegetable oil spread
¼   cup refrigerated or frozen egg product or 1 egg, lightly beaten
5   cooking apples, peeled if desired, cored, and chopped (5 cups)
½   cup dried cherries
2   tablespoons lemon juice
3   tablespoons packed brown sugar
2   tablespoons all-purpose flour
1   teaspoon ground cinnamon
½   teaspoon ground ginger
¼   teaspoon ground cloves

1. Preheat oven to 350°F. In a large bowl combine 1½ cups flour, the oats, granulated sugar, baking powder, and salt. Cut in vegetable oil spread until mixture resembles coarse crumbs. Stir in egg product. Press half of the mixture into a 9×9×2-inch baking pan.

2. In a large bowl combine apples, dried cherries, and lemon juice. Add brown sugar, 2 tablespoons flour, the cinnamon, ginger, and cloves; toss to combine. Layer apple mixture evenly over the crust. Sprinkle with remaining flour mixture.

3. Bake about 50 minutes or until topping is lightly browned and apples are tender. Cool slightly; serve warm. Cut into bars to serve.
MAKES 16 SERVINGS

Coconut-Blueberry Cheesecake Bars

PREP: 30 minutes
BAKE: 26 minutes
CHILL: 3 hours
OVEN: 350°F

NUTRITION FACTS PER SERVING

Calories 109
Fat 6 g
Cholesterol 13 mg
Sodium 79 mg
Carbohydrates 2 g
Fiber 1 g
Protein 2 g

⅓ cup butter
¾ cup finely crushed graham crackers
½ cup flour
½ cup flaked coconut
½ cup ground pecans
¼ cup sugar
1½ 8-ounce packages reduced-fat cream cheese (Neufchâtel), softened
½ cup sugar
1 cup refrigerated or frozen egg product, thawed, or 4 eggs, lightly beaten
1 tablespoon brandy or fat-free milk
1 teaspoon vanilla
2 cups blueberries

1. Preheat oven to 350°F. Lightly grease a 13×9×2-inch baking pan; set aside.

2. For crust, in a small saucepan heat butter over medium heat until the color of light brown sugar. Remove from heat; set aside.

3. In medium bowl stir together graham crackers, flour, coconut, pecans, and ¼ cup sugar. Stir in butter until combined. Evenly press on bottom of prepared pan. Bake for 8 to 10 minutes or until lightly browned.

4. Meanwhile, in large mixing bowl beat cream cheese and ½ cup sugar on medium until combined. Add eggs, brandy, and vanilla. Beat until combined. Pour over hot crust. Sprinkle with blueberries.

5. Bake for 18 to 20 minutes or until center appears set. Cool in pan on a wire rack. Cover and chill. Cut into bars. Store, covered, in the refrigerator. **MAKES 32 SERVINGS**

Chocolate Chunk Cherry Cookies

PREP: 30 minutes
BAKE: 8 minutes per batch
COOL: 1 minute
OVEN: 350°F

NUTRITION FACTS
PER SERVING

Calories 84
Fat 4 g
Cholesterol 0 mg
Sodium 53 mg
Carbohydrates 14 g
Fiber 1 g
Protein 1 g

¼ cup tub-style 60% to 70% vegetable oil spread
⅓ cup packed brown sugar
⅓ cup granulated sugar
½ teaspoon baking soda
⅛ teaspoon salt
¼ cup refrigerated or frozen egg product, thawed, or 1 egg
2 tablespoons unsweetened cocoa powder
1 teaspoon vanilla
⅔ cup all-purpose flour
⅔ cup rolled oats
¼ cup flaxseed meal
4 ounces dark chocolate, chopped
2 ounces white baking chocolate, chopped
½ cup dried tart cherries, coarsely chopped

1. Preheat oven to 350°F. In a large bowl beat vegetable oil spread with an electric mixer on medium to high for 30 seconds. Add brown sugar, granulated sugar, baking soda, and salt. Beat until well mixed, scraping sides of bowl occasionally. Beat in egg, cocoa powder, and vanilla until combined. Beat in flour. Using a wooden spoon, stir in rolled oats and flaxseed meal. Stir in 3 ounces of the dark chocolate, 2 tablespoons of the white chocolate, and ⅓ cup of the cherries.

2. Drop dough by rounded teaspoons 2 inches apart onto ungreased cookie sheets. Top with remaining dark chocolate, white chocolate, and cherries. Bake for 8 to 10 minutes or until edges are set. Let cookies cool on cookie sheets for 1 minute. Transfer cookies to wire racks; let cool.
MAKES 28 SERVINGS

Fruited Oatmeal Cookies

PREP: 25 minutes
BAKE: 9 minutes per batch
OVEN: 375°F

NUTRITION FACTS
PER SERVING

Calories 101
Fat 3 g
Cholesterol 5 mg
Sodium 55 mg
Carbohydrates 1 g
Fiber 1 g
Protein 2 g

2   cups rolled oats
     Nonstick cooking spray
½   cup butter, softened
1½   cups packed brown sugar
¾   teaspoon baking soda
¼   teaspoon salt
¼   teaspoon ground allspice
1   6-ounce carton plain low-fat
     yogurt
½   cup refrigerated or frozen
     egg product or 2 eggs, lightly
     beaten
1   teaspoon vanilla
2¼   cups all-purpose flour
¼   cup snipped dried apricots
¼   cup currants
¼   cup chopped walnuts, toasted
     (see note, page 46)

1. Preheat oven to 375°F. Spread oats in a shallow baking pan. Bake about 10 minutes or until toasted, stirring once; set aside. Lightly coat a cookie sheet with cooking spray or line with parchment paper; set aside.

2. In a large bowl beat butter with an electric mixer on medium to high for 30 seconds. Add brown sugar, baking soda, salt, and allspice; beat until combined. Beat in yogurt, egg product, and vanilla. Beat in as much of the flour as you can with the mixer.

Using a wooden spoon, stir in oats, apricots, currants, walnuts, and any remaining flour. Drop dough by rounded teaspoons 2 inches apart on prepared cookie sheet. Bake 9 to 11 minutes or until edges and bottoms are browned. Transfer cookies to a wire rack; let cool. **MAKES 48 SERVINGS**

Index & Metric

How Recipes Are Analyzed

The Better Homes and Gardens® Test Kitchen uses nutrition-analysis software to determine the nutritional value of a single serving of a recipe. Here are some factors to keep in mind regarding each analysis:

- Analyses do not include optional ingredients.
- The first serving size listed is analyzed when a range is given. For example, if a recipe makes 4 to 6 servings, the Nutrition Facts are based on 4 servings.
- When ingredient choices (such as butter or margarine) appear in a recipe, the first one mentioned is used for analysis.
- When milk is a recipe ingredient, the analysis has been calculated using fat-free (skim) milk unless otherwise noted.

A

Appetizers and snacks
Bourbon-Glazed Cocktail Sausages, 6
Five-Spice Chicken Wings, 7
Honey, Pear, and Gorgonzola Crostini, 8
Pine Nut-White Bean Dip, 18
Rio Grande Dip, 16
Smoky Nut-Stuffed Apricots, 11
Spiced Pear Tea, 22
Spicy Black Bean Crab Cakes, 10
Strawberry-Banana Smoothies, 20
Sunrise Smoothies, 19
Sweet Party Mix, 14
Walnut and Olive Quesadillas, 12
Watermelon, Mango, and Jicama Salsa, 15
Apples
Apple Spice Bars, 254
Apple-Spice Cake, 240
Chicken, Kraut, and Apple Panini, 64
Green Apple Slaw, 218
Spiced Apple Berry Oatmeal, 46
Apricots
Fruited Oatmeal Cookies, 262
Indian Basmati Rice, 234
Smoky Nut-Stuffed Apricots, 11
Artichokes
Cheesy Vegetable Pasta Alfredo, 180
Asian Pork Quesadillas, 124
Asian Pork Sandwiches, 52
Asian Sesame Noodles with Shrimp, 172
Asian Shrimp and Vegetable Soup, 212
Asparagus
Spring Risotto, 236
Avocados
Black Beans and Avocado on Quinoa, 186
Eggs Benedict with Avocado Cream, 26

B

Bacon (pork)
Bacon and Egg Breakfast Wraps, 37
Eggs Benedict with Avocado Cream, 26
Smoky Baked Beans, 237
Bacon (turkey)
Bacon Tomato Melts, 56
Smoky Nut-Stuffed Apricots, 11
Baked Eggs with Roasted Vegetables, 29
Baked Eggs with Tomato, 32
Bananas
Mix and Match Banana Berry Smoothie, 50
Oatmeal Pancakes with Maple Bananas, 42
Strawberry-Banana Smoothies, 20
Banh Mi Vietnamese Sandwiches, 54
Barley
Barley-Stuffed Peppers, 185
Pork Barley Salad, 77
Basil
Bruschetta Burgers, 73
Grilled Plum and Strawberry Kabobs with Sweet Mint Pesto, 252
Beans and lentils. *See also* Green beans
Bean-Tofu Burritos, 190
Black Beans and Avocado on Quinoa, 186
Caribbean Couscous Salad, 232
Caribbean Pork Chili, 204
Chicken Cassoulet with Gremolata, 138
Chicken Chili, 199
Chicken Tostadas, 143
Fiesta Corn Salad, 224
Italian-Style Lentil Soup, 208
Lentil Taco Salad, 192
Moroccan-Spiced Chicken Lentil Stew, 198
Moroccan-Style Simmered Beans, 238
Oven Sausage Cassoulet, 139
Pine Nut-White Bean Dip, 18

Rio Grande Dip, 16
Roasted Tomato and Mushroom Pasta Salad, 90
Smoky Baked Beans, 237
Southwest Breakfast Quesadilla, 36
Spicy Black Bean Crab Cakes, 10
Turkey and Black Bean Chimichangas, 155
Turkey Chipotle Chili, 203
White Bean Moussaka, 189
Beef
Beef Stroganoff, 102
Beefy Stuffed Shells, 108
Cheeseburger Soup, 206
Cheesesteaks with Sweet Peppers and Mushrooms, 105
Chipotle Picante Meat Loaf with Cilantro, 109
Grilled Beef Tenderloin with Mediterranean Relish, 92
Grilled Chili Burgers, 58
Grilled Flank Steak Salad, 78
Grilled New York Strip Steaks, 94
Hearty Beef and Vegetable Stew, 207
Herbed Steak with Balsamic Sauce, 104
Hot Italian Beef Salad, 80
Italian Beef and Polenta, 100
Italian Shepherd's Pie, 106
Korean Barbecued Flank Steak, 97
Moroccan Beef and Pumpkin Bake, 96
Open-Face Shredded Beef Sandwiches, 60
Saucy Pot Roast with Noodles, 93
Sesame Ginger Beef Stir-Fry, 101
Texas Beef with Butternut Squash, 98
Berries
Coconut-Blueberry Cheesecake Bars, 256
Cranberry Vinaigrette, 225
Grilled Plum and Strawberry Kabobs with Sweet Mint Pesto, 252
Layered Fruit Salad, 48
Lemon-Berry Pudding Cake, 250
Mix and Match Banana Berry Smoothie, 50
Roasted Pork with Blackberry Sauce, 117
Spiced Apple Berry Oatmeal, 46
Strawberry-Banana Smoothies, 20
Superfoods Salad, 89
Black Beans and Avocado on Quinoa, 186
Blackberries
Mix and Match Banana Berry Smoothie, 50
Roasted Pork with Blackberry Sauce, 117
Spiced Apple Berry Oatmeal, 46
Blackened Salmon with Vegetables, 167
Black Tie Cake, 242
Blueberries
Coconut-Blueberry Cheesecake Bars, 256
Layered Fruit Salad, 48
Lemon-Berry Pudding Cake, 250
Mix and Match Banana Berry Smoothie, 50

Spiced Apple Berry Oatmeal, 46
Superfoods Salad, 89

Bok choy
Asian Sesame Noodles with Shrimp, 172
Asian Shrimp and Vegetable Soup, 212
Korean Barbecued Flank Steak, 97
Bourbon-Glazed Cocktail Sausages, 6

Breakfast dishes
Bacon and Egg Breakfast Wraps, 37
Baked Eggs with Roasted Vegetables, 29
Baked Eggs with Tomato, 32
Breakfast Pita Pizza, 38
Citrus Mock Mimosas, 49
Crustless Spinach-and-Mushroom
   Quiche, 28
Eggs Benedict with Avocado Cream, 26
Green Eggs and Ham Breakfast
   Burritos, 34
Layered Fruit Salad, 48
Loaded Hash Browns, 25
Mix and Match Banana Berry
   Smoothie, 50
Mocha Coffee Cake, 44
Oatmeal Pancakes with Maple
   Bananas, 42
Peachy Granola Muffins, 45
Poached Eggs on Soft Polenta, 30
Poblano Tofu Scramble, 40
Salmon-Dill Omelet, 33
Sausage Skillet, 41
Southwest Breakfast Quesadilla, 36
Spiced Apple Berry Oatmeal, 46
Sweet Potato and Turkey Sausage
   Hash, 24

Broccoli
Baked Eggs with Roasted Vegetables, 29
Blackened Salmon with Vegetables, 167
Broccoli Slaw, 53
Chicken-Pasta Toss, 135
Gingered Lemon Broccoli Salad, 216
Lemon-Dill Cauliflower and
   Broccoli, 229
Sesame Ginger Beef Stir-Fry, 101
Simple Hoisin Chicken, 140
Browned Butter Pastry, 246
Bruschetta Burgers, 73

Bulgur
Chilled Salmon and Tabbouleh, 86
Dried Fruit, Chicken, and Bulgur
   Pilaf, 132
Smoked Turkey and Bulgur, 152

Burgers
Bruschetta Burgers, 73
Grilled Chili Burgers, 58

Burritos
Bean-Tofu Burritos, 190
Green Eggs and Ham Breakfast
   Burritos, 34

C

Cabbage and bok choy
Asian Pork Quesadillas, 124
Asian Sesame Noodles with Shrimp, 172
Asian Shrimp and Vegetable Soup, 212

Green Apple Slaw, 218
Korean Barbecued Flank Steak, 97
Spicy Vegetable Fried Rice, 184
Tropical Chicken Salad Wraps, 65

Cakes
Apple-Spice Cake, 240
Black Tie Cake, 242
Ginger-Spiced Chocolate Cake, 241
Lemon-Berry Pudding Cake, 250
Lemon Poppy Seed Snack Cake, 244
May Basket Cupcakes, 245
Mocha Coffee Cake, 44
Caper Mayonnaise, 168
Caribbean Couscous Salad, 232
Caribbean Pork Chili, 204

Carrots
Asian Sesame Noodles with Shrimp, 172
Asian Shrimp and Vegetable Soup, 212
Cinnamon-Almond Topped Carrots, 221
Creamy Chicken Noodle Soup, 194
Hearty Beef and Vegetable Stew, 207
Italian-Style Lentil Soup, 208
Moroccan Lamb Tagine, 125
Rosemary Turkey Roast with
   Vegetables, 150
Spicy Vegetable Fried Rice, 184
Catfish Salad, 84

Cauliflower
Blackened Salmon with Vegetables, 167
Cheesy Vegetable Pasta Alfredo, 180
Lemon-Dill Cauliflower and Broccoli, 229

Cheese
Bacon Tomato Melts, 56
Breakfast Pita Pizza, 38
Bruschetta Burgers, 73
Cheese- and Date-Stuffed Chicken
   Breasts, 130
Cheeseburger Soup, 206
Cheesesteaks with Sweet Peppers
   and Mushrooms, 105
Cheesy Vegetable Pasta Alfredo, 180
Chicken, Macaroni, and Cheese, 134
Chicken Taco Casserole, 146
Coconut-Blueberry Cheesecake
   Bars, 256
Crustless Spinach-and-Mushroom
   Quiche, 28
Eggplant Parmesan Stacks, 188
Honey, Pear, and Gorgonzola Crostini, 8
Hot Ham and Pear Melts, 57
Italian Meatball Rolls, 66
Italian Shepherd's Pie, 106
Open-Face Shredded Beef
   Sandwiches, 60
Parmesan Baked Fish, 163
Penne with Ricotta and Summer
   Vegetables, 182
Rio Grande Dip, 16
Salmon Melts, 70
Turkey Orzo with Dried Cherries and
   Feta Cheese, 151
Walnut and Olive Quesadillas, 12

Cherries
Chocolate Chunk Cherry Cookies, 261

Turkey Orzo with Dried Cherries and
   Feta Cheese, 151

Chicken
Cheese- and Date-Stuffed Chicken
   Breasts, 130
Chicken, Kraut, and Apple Panini, 64
Chicken, Macaroni, and Cheese, 134
Chicken and Cornmeal Dumplings, 142
Chicken and Portobellos with
   Mustard Cream, 136
Chicken and Sweet Pepper Linguine
   Alfredo, 131
Chicken Cassoulet with Gremolata, 138
Chicken Chili, 199
Chicken-Pasta Toss, 135
Chicken-Squash Noodle Soup, 195
Chicken Taco Casserole, 146
Chicken Tostadas, 143
Cream of Chicken and Rice
   Florentine, 196
Creamy Chicken Noodle Soup, 194
Dried Fruit, Chicken, and Bulgur
   Pilaf, 132
Five-Spice Chicken Wings, 7
Grilled Chicken, Spinach, and Pear
   Pitas, 62
Moroccan Chicken, 144
Moroccan-Spiced Chicken Lentil
   Stew, 198
Oven Sausage Cassoulet, 139
Peanut Noodles with Chicken and
   Vegetables, 148
Simple Hoisin Chicken, 140
Spicy Egg-Stuffed Peppers, 147
Superfoods Salad, 89
Tropical Chicken Salad Wraps, 65

Chili
Caribbean Pork Chili, 204
Chicken Chili, 199
Turkey Chipotle Chili, 203
Chilled Salmon and Tabbouleh, 86
Chimichangas, Turkey and Black Bean, 155
Chimichurri, 58
Chipotle Picante Meat Loaf with
   Cilantro, 109

Chocolate
Black Tie Cake, 242
Chocolate Chunk Cherry Cookies, 261
Ginger-Spiced Chocolate Cake, 241
Layered Brownies, 257
Mocha Coffee Cake, 44
Soft Chocolate Chip Cookies, 260
Tiramisu Shots, 253

Cilantro
Chimichurri, 58
Chipotle Picante Meat Loaf with
   Cilantro, 109
Cilantro Dressing, 78
Corn on the Cob with Cilantro-Lime
   Butter, 226
Cinnamon-Almond Topped Carrots, 221
Citrus Mock Mimosas, 49
Coconut-Blueberry Cheesecake Bars, 256
Coconut Shrimp with Mango Rice Pilaf, 174

Coffee Cake, Mocha, 44

Cookies and bars
  Apple Spice Bars, 254
  Chocolate Chunk Cherry Cookies, 261
  Coconut-Blueberry Cheesecake
    Bars, 256
  Fruited Oatmeal Cookies, 262
  Layered Brownies, 257
  Pumpkin Bars, 258
  Soft Chocolate Chip Cookies, 260

Corn
  Corn on the Cob with Cilantro-Lime
    Butter, 226
  Fiesta Corn Salad, 224
  Grilled Flank Steak Salad, 78
  Seafood-Corn Chowder, 214
  Turkey Chopped Salad with Orange-
    Poppy Seed Dressing, 81

Cornmeal
  Chicken and Cornmeal Dumplings, 142
  Moroccan Beef and Pumpkin Bake, 96
  Poached Eggs on Soft Polenta, 30

Couscous
  Caribbean Couscous Salad, 232
  Moroccan Beef and Pumpkin Bake, 96
  Pork Tenderloin with Sweet-Spiced
    Onions, 110
Crab Cakes, Spicy Black Bean, 10
Cranberry Vinaigrette, 225
Cream of Chicken and Rice Florentine, 196
Creamy Chicken Noodle Soup, 194
Crunchy Zucchini and Tomato, 220
Crustless Spinach-and-Mushroom
  Quiche, 28

Cucumbers
  Cucumber-Yogurt Sauce, 154
  Greek Garden Pasta Salad, 230
  Salmon and Spinach Salad with
    Flaxseed Dressing, 85
Curried Sea Scallops, 170

D

Dates
  Date-and-Cheese-Stuffed Chicken
    Breasts, 130
  Moroccan Lamb Tagine, 125

Desserts
  Apple Spice Bars, 254
  Apple-Spice Cake, 240
  Black Tie Cake, 242
  Chocolate Chunk Cherry Cookies, 261
  Coconut-Blueberry Cheesecake
    Bars, 256
  Fruited Oatmeal Cookies, 262
  Ginger-Spiced Chocolate Cake, 241
  Grilled Plum and Strawberry Kabobs
    with Sweet Mint Pesto, 252
  Layered Brownies, 257
  Lemon-Berry Pudding Cake, 250
  Lemon Poppy Seed Snack Cake, 244
  Lemon Tart with Ginger-Oat Crust, 248
  May Basket Cupcakes, 245
  Plum Galettes, 246

Pumpkin Bars, 258
  Soft Chocolate Chip Cookies, 260
  Tiramisu Shots, 253
  Vanilla Meringue Tarts, 249
Dijon Vinaigrette, 77
Dipping Sauce, 178

Dips and spreads
  Caper Mayonnaise, 168
  Pine Nut-White Bean Dip, 18
  Rio Grande Dip, 16
  Watermelon, Mango, and Jicama
    Salsa, 15
Dried Fruit, Chicken, and Bulgur Pilaf, 132

Drinks
  Citrus Mock Mimosas, 49
  Mix and Match Banana Berry
    Smoothie, 50
  Spiced Pear Tea, 22
  Strawberry-Banana Smoothies, 20
  Sunrise Smoothies, 19

E

Eggplant
  Eggplant Parmesan Stacks, 188
  Grilled Beef Tenderloin with
    Mediterranean Relish, 92
  Ratatouille Stew, 210
  Roasted Vegetable Pitas, 74
  White Bean Moussaka, 189

Eggs
  Bacon and Egg Breakfast Wraps, 37
  Baked Eggs with Roasted Vegetables, 29
  Baked Eggs with Tomato, 32
  Crustless Spinach-and-Mushroom
    Quiche, 28
  Eggs Benedict with Avocado Cream, 26
  Green Eggs and Ham Breakfast
    Burritos, 34
  Poached Eggs on Soft Polenta, 30
  Salmon-Dill Omelet, 33
  Southwest Breakfast Quesadilla, 36
  Spicy Egg-Stuffed Peppers, 147
  Spicy Vegetable Fried Rice, 184

F

Farmer's Market Salad Platter, 217
Fennel
  Orange, Fennel, and Olive Salad with
    Cranberry Vinaigrette, 225
  Sour Cream-Fennel Pork
    Tenderloins, 113
  Spring Risotto, 236
Fiesta Corn Salad, 224
Fish. See also Salmon
  Catfish Salad, 84
  Grilled Fish Tacos with Pineapple
    Salsa, 164
  Grilled Halibut Sarandeado, 159
  Pan Bagnat, 68
  Parmesan Baked Fish, 163
  Red Snapper with Sweet Peppers, 158
  Seafood-Corn Chowder, 214
  Snapper Piccata, 162

Tuna and Hummus Wrap, 69
  Tuscan Tuna with Tomato Salad, 166
  Wasabi-Glazed Whitefish, 160
Five-Spice Chicken Wings, 7
Flaxseed Dressing, 85
Fruit. See also Berries; specific fruits
  Dried Fruit, Chicken, and Bulgur
    Pilaf, 132
  Fruited Oatmeal Cookies, 262
  Fruit Salad with a Crunch, 222
  May Basket Cupcakes, 245
  Vanilla Meringue Tarts, 249

G

Garlic
  Gremolata, 138
  Lamb Chops with Garlic and
    Lavender, 128
Ginger
  Gingered Lemon Broccoli Salad, 216
  Ginger-Lime Vinaigrette, 232
  Ginger-Oat Crust, 248
  Ginger-Spiced Chocolate Cake, 241
  Sesame Ginger Beef Stir-Fry, 101
Grains. See also Oats; Rice
  Barley-Stuffed Peppers, 185
  Black Beans and Avocado on
    Quinoa, 186
  Chicken and Cornmeal Dumplings, 142
  Chilled Salmon and Tabbouleh, 86
  Dried Fruit, Chicken, and Bulgur
    Pilaf, 132
  Moroccan Beef and Pumpkin Bake, 96
  Poached Eggs on Soft Polenta, 30
  Pork Barley Salad, 77
  Smoked Turkey and Bulgur, 152
Greek Garden Pasta Salad, 230
Greek Lamb with Spinach and Orzo, 126
Green Apple Slaw, 218
Green beans
  Cheesy Vegetable Pasta Alfredo, 180
  Farmer's Market Salad Platter, 217
  Green Beans with Peppers and
    Pineapple, 228
  Italian Beef and Polenta, 100
  Spring Risotto, 236
  Vegetable Garden Soup with Turkey, 202
Green Eggs and Ham Breakfast
  Burritos, 34
Greens. See also Spinach
  Catfish Salad, 84
  Chilled Salmon and Tabbouleh, 86
  Hot Italian Beef Salad, 80
  Lemon-Sage Pork Salad, 76
  Lentil Taco Salad, 192
  Orange, Fennel, and Olive Salad with
    Cranberry Vinaigrette, 225
  Pork Barley Salad, 77
  Spring Risotto, 236
  Turkey Chopped Salad with Orange-
    Poppy Seed Dressing, 81
Gremolata, 138

Grilled dishes

Curried Sea Scallops, 170
Grilled Beef Tenderloin with
  Mediterranean Relish, 92
Grilled Chicken, Spinach, and Pear
  Pitas, 62
Grilled Chili Burgers, 58
Grilled Fish Tacos with Pineapple
  Salsa, 164
Grilled Flank Steak Salad, 78
Grilled Halibut Sarandeado, 159
Grilled New York Strip Steaks, 94
Grilled Plum and Strawberry Kabobs
  with Sweet Mint Pesto, 252
Grilled Turkey Gyros, 154
Korean Barbecued Flank Steak, 97
Lamb Chops with Garlic and
  Lavender, 128
Lemon-Dill Cauliflower and Broccoli, 229
Moroccan Chicken, 144
Pork Barley Salad, 77
Pork Skewers with Fruit Glaze, 122
Roasted Pork with Blackberry
  Sauce, 117
Salmon and Spinach Salad with
  Flaxseed Dressing, 85
Skewered Shrimp Scampi, 175
Tuscan Tuna with Tomato Salad, 166
Wasabi-Glazed Whitefish, 160
Zucchini Fritters with Orange
  Shrimp, 178

H

Halibut

Grilled Halibut Sarandeado, 159
Seafood-Corn Chowder, 214

Ham

Green Eggs and Ham Breakfast
  Burritos, 34
Hot Ham and Pear Melts, 57
Hearty Beef and Vegetable Stew, 207

Herbs. *See also specific herbs*

Chimichurri, 58
Herbed Steak with Balsamic Sauce, 104
Herb-Scented Tuscan Pork Loin, 112
Homemade Walking Tacos, 156
Honey, Pear, and Gorgonzola Crostini, 8
Hot Ham and Pear Melts, 57
Hot Italian Beef Salad, 80

I

Indian Basmati Rice, 234
Italian Beef and Polenta, 100
Italian Meatball Rolls, 66
Italian Pork Chops, 120
Italian Shepherd's Pie, 106
Italian-Style Lentil Soup, 208

K

Kiwifruit

Fruit Salad with a Crunch, 222
Layered Fruit Salad, 48
Korean Barbecued Flank Steak, 97

L

Lamb

Greek Lamb with Spinach and Orzo, 126
Lamb Chops with Garlic and
  Lavender, 128
Moroccan Lamb Tagine, 125
Layered Brownies, 257
Layered Fruit Salad, 48
Lemon-Berry Pudding Cake, 250
Lemon-Dill Cauliflower and Broccoli, 229
Lemon Glaze, 244
Lemon Poppy Seed Snack Cake, 244
Lemon-Sage Pork Salad, 76
Lemon Tart with Ginger-Oat Crust, 248

Lentils

Italian-Style Lentil Soup, 208
Lentil Taco Salad, 192
Moroccan-Spiced Chicken Lentil
  Stew, 198
Lime-Honey Dressing, 222
Lime-Onion Cream, 10
Loaded Hash Browns, 25

M

Main dishes (meat)

Asian Pork Quesadillas, 124
Beef Stroganoff, 102
Beefy Stuffed Shells, 108
Cheesesteaks with Sweet Peppers
  and Mushrooms, 105
Chipotle Picante Meat Loaf with
  Cilantro, 109
Greek Lamb with Spinach and Orzo, 126
Grilled Beef Tenderloin with
  Mediterranean Relish, 92
Grilled Flank Steak Salad, 78
Grilled New York Strip Steaks, 94
Herbed Steak with Balsamic Sauce, 104
Herb-Scented Tuscan Pork Loin, 112
Hot Italian Beef Salad, 80
Italian Beef and Polenta, 100
Italian Pork Chops, 120
Italian Shepherd's Pie, 106
Korean Barbecued Flank Steak, 97
Lamb Chops with Garlic and
  Lavender, 128
Lemon-Sage Pork Salad, 76
Moroccan Beef and Pumpkin Bake, 96
Moroccan Lamb Tagine, 125
Pork Barley Salad, 77
Pork Loin with Creamy Pesto Sauce, 116
Pork Skewers with Fruit Glaze, 122
Pork Tenderloin with Sweet-Spiced
  Onions, 110
Roasted Pork with Blackberry Sauce, 117
Roast Pork with Romesco Sauce, 118
Root Beer-Marinated Pork Tenderloin
  with Sweet Potatoes, 114
Saucy Pot Roast with Noodles, 93
Sesame Ginger Beef Stir-Fry, 101
Skillet Roasted Potatoes with Pork
  and Wilted Arugula, 121

Sour Cream-Fennel Pork
  Tenderloins, 113
Texas Beef with Butternut Squash, 98

Main dishes (poultry)

Cheese- and Date-Stuffed Chicken
  Breasts, 130
Chicken, Macaroni, and Cheese, 134
Chicken and Cornmeal Dumplings, 142
Chicken and Portobellos with
  Mustard Cream, 136
Chicken and Sweet Pepper Linguine
  Alfredo, 131
Chicken Cassoulet with Gremolata, 138
Chicken-Pasta Toss, 135
Chicken Taco Casserole, 146
Chicken Tostadas, 143
Dried Fruit, Chicken, and Bulgur
  Pilaf, 132
Grilled Turkey Gyros, 154
Homemade Walking Tacos, 156
Moroccan Chicken, 144
Oven Sausage Cassoulet, 139
Peanut Noodles with Chicken and
  Vegetables, 148
Rosemary Turkey Roast with
  Vegetables, 150
Simple Hoisin Chicken, 140
Smoked Turkey and Bulgur, 152
Spicy Egg-Stuffed Peppers, 147
Superfoods Salad, 89
Turkey and Black Bean
  Chimichangas, 155
Turkey Chopped Salad with Orange-
  Poppy Seed Dressing, 81
Turkey Orzo with Dried Cherries and
  Feta Cheese, 151
Turkey Wild Rice Salad, 82

Main dishes (salads)

Catfish Salad, 84
Chilled Salmon and Tabbouleh, 86
Grilled Flank Steak Salad, 78
Hot Italian Beef Salad, 80
Lemon-Sage Pork Salad, 76
Pork Barley Salad, 77
Roasted Tomato and Mushroom
  Pasta Salad, 90
Salmon and Spinach Salad with
  Flaxseed Dressing, 85
Superfoods Salad, 89
Turkey Chopped Salad with Orange-
  Poppy Seed Dressing, 81
Turkey Wild Rice Salad, 82
Warm Yukon Gold and Sweet Potato
  Salad, 88

Main dishes (seafood)

Asian Sesame Noodles with Shrimp, 172
Blackened Salmon with Vegetables, 167
Catfish Salad, 84
Chilled Salmon and Tabbouleh, 86
Coconut Shrimp with Mango Rice
  Pilaf, 174
Curried Sea Scallops, 170
Grilled Fish Tacos with Pineapple
  Salsa, 164

Grilled Halibut Sarandeado, 159
Orange-Balsamic Marinated Shrimp, 171
Parmesan Baked Fish, 163
Red Snapper with Sweet Peppers, 158
Salmon and Spinach Salad with
    Flaxseed Dressing, 85
Salmon Cakes with Caper
    Mayonnaise, 168
Shrimp and Mushroom Pasta, 176
Skewered Shrimp Scampi, 175
Snapper Piccata, 162
Tuscan Tuna with Tomato Salad, 166
Wasabi-Glazed Whitefish, 160
Zucchini Fritters with Orange
    Shrimp, 178

Main dishes (vegetarian)
Barley-Stuffed Peppers, 185
Bean-Tofu Burritos, 190
Black Beans and Avocado on
    Quinoa, 186
Cheesy Vegetable Pasta Alfredo, 180
Eggplant Parmesan Stacks, 188
Lentil Taco Salad, 192
Penne with Ricotta and Summer
    Vegetables, 182
Penne with Walnuts and Peppers, 181
Spicy Vegetable Fried Rice, 184
White Bean Moussaka, 189

Mango
Caribbean Couscous Salad, 232
Caribbean Pork Chili, 204
Coconut Shrimp with Mango Rice
    Pilaf, 174
Layered Fruit Salad, 48
Watermelon, Mango, and Jicama
    Salsa, 15
Mashed Potatoes, 106
May Basket Cupcakes, 245
Meat. See Beef; Lamb; Pork
Meatball Rolls, Italian, 66

Meatless burger patties
Bruschetta Burgers, 73
Meat Loaf, Chipotle Picante, with
    Cilantro, 109

Melon
Sunrise Smoothies, 19
Watermelon, Mango, and Jicama
    Salsa, 15
Watermelon Soup with Fresh Mint, 211
Meringue Tarts, Vanilla, 249
Mexican-Style Roast Sandwiches, 61
Mint Pesto, Sweet, Grilled Plum and
    Strawberry Kabobs with, 252
Mix and Match Banana Berry Smoothie, 50
Mocha Coffee Cake, 44
Moroccan Beef and Pumpkin Bake, 96
Moroccan Chicken, 144
Moroccan Lamb Tagine, 125
Moroccan-Spiced Chicken Lentil Stew, 198
Moroccan-Style Simmered Beans, 238
Mousse, White Chocolate, 242
Muffins, Peachy Granola, 45

Mushrooms
Asian Shrimp and Vegetable Soup, 212
Barley-Stuffed Peppers, 185
Beef Stroganoff, 102
Cheesesteaks with Sweet Peppers
    and Mushrooms, 105
Chicken and Portobellos with
    Mustard Cream, 136
Creamy Chicken Noodle Soup, 194
Crustless Spinach-and-Mushroom
    Quiche, 28
Roasted Tomato and Mushroom
    Pasta Salad, 90
Shrimp and Mushroom Pasta, 176

Noodles
Asian Sesame Noodles with Shrimp, 172
Beef Stroganoff, 102
Chicken-Squash Noodle Soup, 195
Creamy Chicken Noodle Soup, 194
Saucy Pot Roast with Noodles, 93

Nuts
Penne with Walnuts and Peppers, 181
Pine Nut-White Bean Dip, 18
Smoky Nut-Stuffed Apricots, 11
Walnut and Olive Quesadillas, 12

Oatmeal Pancakes with Maple Bananas, 42
Oats
Apple Spice Bars, 254
Fruited Oatmeal Cookies, 262
Ginger-Oat Crust, 248
Layered Brownies, 257
Oatmeal Pancakes with Maple
    Bananas, 42
Soft Chocolate Chip Cookies, 260
Spiced Apple Berry Oatmeal, 46

Olives
Greek Garden Pasta Salad, 230
Moroccan Lamb Tagine, 125
Orange, Fennel, and Olive Salad with
    Cranberry Vinaigrette, 225
Walnut and Olive Quesadillas, 12
Omelet, Salmon-Dill, 33
Open-Face Shredded Beef Sandwiches, 60

Oranges
Citrus Mock Mimosas, 49
Dipping Sauce, 178
Layered Fruit Salad, 48
Moroccan Chicken, 144
Orange, Fennel, and Olive Salad with
    Cranberry Vinaigrette, 225
Orange-Balsamic Marinated Shrimp, 171
Orange-Poppy Seed Dressing, 81
Oven Sausage Cassoulet, 139

Pan Bagnat, 68
Pancakes, Oatmeal, with Maple
    Bananas, 42

Parmesan Baked Fish, 163
Parsley
Chimichurri, 58
Gremolata, 138
Pasta. See also Couscous; Noodles
Beefy Stuffed Shells, 108
Cheesy Vegetable Pasta Alfredo, 180
Chicken, Macaroni, and Cheese, 134
Chicken and Sweet Pepper Linguine
    Alfredo, 131
Chicken-Pasta Toss, 135
Greek Garden Pasta Salad, 230
Greek Lamb with Spinach and Orzo, 126
Italian-Style Lentil Soup, 208
Peanut Noodles with Chicken and
    Vegetables, 148
Penne with Ricotta and Summer
    Vegetables, 182
Penne with Walnuts and Peppers, 181
Roasted Tomato and Mushroom
    Pasta Salad, 90
Shrimp and Mushroom Pasta, 176
Skewered Shrimp Scampi, 175
Turkey Orzo with Dried Cherries and
    Feta Cheese, 151

Pastry
Browned Butter Pastry, 246
Ginger-Oat Crust, 248
Peaches
Mix and Match Banana Berry
    Smoothie, 50
Peachy Granola Muffins, 45
Peanut butter
Peanut Noodles with Chicken and
    Vegetables, 148
Peanut Sauce, 124
Pears
Fruit Salad with a Crunch, 222
Grilled Chicken, Spinach, and Pear
    Pitas, 62
Honey, Pear, and Gorgonzola Crostini, 8
Hot Ham and Pear Melts, 57
Spiced Pear Tea, 22
Peas
Asian Sesame Noodles with Shrimp, 172
Asian Shrimp and Vegetable Soup, 212
Indian Basmati Rice, 234
Italian-Style Lentil Soup, 208
Spicy Vegetable Fried Rice, 184
Penne with Ricotta and Summer
    Vegetables, 182
Penne with Walnuts and Peppers, 181
Peppers
Barley-Stuffed Peppers, 185
Breakfast Pita Pizza, 38
Cheesesteaks with Sweet Peppers
    and Mushrooms, 105
Chicken and Sweet Pepper Linguine
    Alfredo, 131
Green Beans with Peppers and
    Pineapple, 228
Grilled Beef Tenderloin with
    Mediterranean Relish, 92

Penne with Walnuts and Peppers, 181
Poblano Tofu Scramble, 40
Red Hot Pepper Vinaigrette, 76
Red Snapper with Sweet Peppers, 158
Romesco Sauce, 118
Spicy Egg-Stuffed Peppers, 147

Pineapple
Fruit Salad with a Crunch, 222
Green Beans with Peppers and
Pineapple, 228
Grilled Fish Tacos with Pineapple
Salsa, 164
Tropical Chicken Salad Wraps, 65
Pine Nut-White Bean Dip, 18
Pizza, Breakfast Pita, 38

Plums
Grilled Plum and Strawberry Kabobs
with Sweet Mint Pesto, 252
Plum Galettes, 246
Poached Eggs on Soft Polenta, 30
Poblano Tofu Scramble, 40

Polenta
Catfish Salad, 84
Italian Beef and Polenta, 100
Poached Eggs on Soft Polenta, 30

Pork. *See also* Bacon (pork); Ham
Asian Pork Quesadillas, 124
Asian Pork Sandwiches, 52
Banh Mi Vietnamese Sandwiches, 54
Bourbon-Glazed Cocktail Sausages, 6
Caribbean Pork Chili, 204
Grilled Chili Burgers, 58
Herb-Scented Tuscan Pork Loin, 112
Italian Pork Chops, 120
Lemon-Sage Pork Salad, 76
Mexican-Style Roast Sandwiches, 61
Oven Sausage Cassoulet, 139
Pork Barley Salad, 77
Pork Loin with Creamy Pesto Sauce, 116
Pork Skewers with Fruit Glaze, 122
Pork Tenderloin Sandwiches, 53
Pork Tenderloin with Sweet-Spiced
Onions, 110
Roasted Pork with Blackberry Sauce, 117
Roast Pork with Romesco Sauce, 118
Root Beer-Marinated Pork Tenderloin
with Sweet Potatoes, 114
Skillet Roasted Potatoes with Pork
and Wilted Arugula, 121
Sour Cream-Fennel Pork
Tenderloins, 113
Spicy Egg-Stuffed Peppers, 147

Potatoes. *See also* Sweet potatoes
Farmer's Market Salad Platter, 217
Italian Shepherd's Pie, 106
Loaded Hash Browns, 25
Mashed Potatoes, 106
Rosemary Turkey Roast with
Vegetables, 150
Sausage Skillet, 41
Skillet Roasted Potatoes with Pork
and Wilted Arugula, 121

Sweet Potato and Turkey Sausage
Hash, 24
Vegetable Garden Soup with Turkey, 202
Warm Yukon Gold and Sweet Potato
Salad, 88
Poultry. *See* Chicken; Turkey
Pumpkin
Moroccan Beef and Pumpkin Bake, 96
Pumpkin Bars, 258

Quesadillas
Asian Pork Quesadillas, 124
Southwest Breakfast Quesadilla, 36
Walnut and Olive Quesadillas, 12
Quiche, Crustless Spinach-and-
Mushroom, 28
Quinoa, Black Beans and Avocado on, 186

Raspberries
Lemon-Berry Pudding Cake, 250
Mix and Match Banana Berry
Smoothie, 50
Spiced Apple Berry Oatmeal, 46
Ratatouille Stew, 210
Red Hot Pepper Vinaigrette, 76
Red Snapper with Sweet Peppers, 158
Rice
Chipotle Picante Meat Loaf with
Cilantro, 109
Coconut Shrimp with Mango Rice
Pilaf, 174
Cream of Chicken and Rice
Florentine, 196
Indian Basmati Rice, 234
Spanish-Style Rice, 233
Spicy Vegetable Fried Rice, 184
Spring Risotto, 236
Turkey Wild Rice Salad, 82
Turkey Wild Rice Soup, 200
Rio Grande Dip, 16
Risotto, Spring, 236
Roasted Pork with Blackberry Sauce, 117
Roasted Tomato and Mushroom Pasta
Salad, 90
Roasted Vegetable Pitas, 74
Roast Pork with Romesco Sauce, 118
Romesco Sauce, 118
Root Beer-Marinated Pork Tenderloin
with Sweet Potatoes, 114
Rosemary Turkey Roast with
Vegetables, 150

Salad dressings
Cilantro Dressing, 78
Cranberry Vinaigrette, 225
Dijon Vinaigrette, 77
Flaxseed Dressing, 85
Ginger-Lime Vinaigrette, 232

Lime-Honey Dressing, 222
Orange-Poppy Seed Dressing, 81
Red Hot Pepper Vinaigrette, 76
Salads (main dish)
Catfish Salad, 84
Chilled Salmon and Tabbouleh, 86
Grilled Flank Steak Salad, 78
Hot Italian Beef Salad, 80
Lemon-Sage Pork Salad, 76
Lentil Taco Salad, 192
Pork Barley Salad, 77
Roasted Tomato and Mushroom
Pasta Salad, 90
Salmon and Spinach Salad with
Flaxseed Dressing, 85
Superfoods Salad, 89
Turkey Chopped Salad with Orange-
Poppy Seed Dressing, 81
Turkey Wild Rice Salad, 82
Warm Yukon Gold and Sweet Potato
Salad, 88
Salads (side dish)
Broccoli Slaw, 53
Caribbean Couscous Salad, 232
Farmer's Market Salad Platter, 217
Fiesta Corn Salad, 224
Fruit Salad with a Crunch, 222
Gingered Lemon Broccoli Salad, 216
Greek Garden Pasta Salad, 230
Green Apple Slaw, 218
Layered Fruit Salad, 48
Orange, Fennel, and Olive Salad with
Cranberry Vinaigrette, 225
Salmon
Blackened Salmon with Vegetables, 167
Chilled Salmon and Tabbouleh, 86
Parmesan Baked Fish, 163
Salmon and Spinach Salad with
Flaxseed Dressing, 85
Salmon Cakes with Caper
Mayonnaise, 168
Salmon-Dill Omelet, 33
Salmon Melts, 70
Salsa, Watermelon, Mango, and
Jicama, 15
Sandwiches and burgers
Asian Pork Sandwiches, 52
Bacon and Egg Breakfast Wraps, 37
Bacon Tomato Melts, 56
Banh Mi Vietnamese Sandwiches, 54
Bruschetta Burgers, 73
Cheesesteaks with Sweet Peppers
and Mushrooms, 105
Chicken, Kraut, and Apple Panini, 64
Eggplant Parmesan Stacks, 188
Grilled Chicken, Spinach, and Pear
Pitas, 62
Grilled Chili Burgers, 58
Grilled Turkey Gyros, 154
Hot Ham and Pear Melts, 57
Italian Meatball Rolls, 66
Mexican-Style Roast Sandwiches, 61
Open-Face Shredded Beef
Sandwiches, 60

Pan Bagnat, 68
Pork Tenderloin Sandwiches, 53
Roasted Vegetable Pitas, 74
Salmon Melts, 70
Shrimp Po'Boys, 72
Tropical Chicken Salad Wraps, 65
Tuna and Hummus Wrap, 69
Sauces and toppings
Avocado Cream, 26
Chimichurri, 58
Cucumber-Yogurt Sauce, 154
Dipping Sauce, 178
Gremolata, 138
Lime-Onion Cream, 10
Peanut Sauce, 124
Romesco Sauce, 118
Saucy Pot Roast with Noodles, 93
Sausages
Bourbon-Glazed Cocktail Sausages, 6
Loaded Hash Browns, 25
Oven Sausage Cassoulet, 139
Rio Grande Dip, 16
Sausage Skillet, 41
Spicy Egg-Stuffed Peppers, 147
Sweet Potato and Turkey Sausage
    Hash, 24
Warm Yukon Gold and Sweet Potato
    Salad, 88
Scallops
Curried Sea Scallops, 170
Seafood-Corn Chowder, 214
Seafood. *See* Fish; Shellfish
Sesame Ginger Beef Stir-Fry, 101
Shellfish. *See also* Shrimp
Curried Sea Scallops, 170
Seafood-Corn Chowder, 214
Spicy Black Bean Crab Cakes, 10
Shrimp
Asian Sesame Noodles with Shrimp, 172
Asian Shrimp and Vegetable Soup, 212
Coconut Shrimp with Mango Rice
    Pilaf, 174
Orange-Balsamic Marinated Shrimp, 171
Shrimp and Mushroom Pasta, 176
Shrimp Po'Boys, 72
Skewered Shrimp Scampi, 175
Zucchini Fritters with Orange
    Shrimp, 178
Side dishes
Broccoli Slaw, 53
Caribbean Couscous Salad, 232
Cinnamon-Almond Topped Carrots, 221
Corn on the Cob with Cilantro-Lime
    Butter, 226
Crunchy Zucchini and Tomato, 220
Farmer's Market Salad Platter, 217
Fiesta Corn Salad, 224
Fruit Salad with a Crunch, 222
Gingered Lemon Broccoli Salad, 216
Greek Garden Pasta Salad, 230
Green Apple Slaw, 218
Green Beans with Peppers and
    Pineapple, 228

Indian Basmati Rice, 234
Layered Fruit Salad, 48
Lemon-Dill Cauliflower and Broccoli, 229
Mashed Potatoes, 106
Moroccan-Style Simmered Beans, 238
Orange, Fennel, and Olive Salad with
    Cranberry Vinaigrette, 225
Smoky Baked Beans, 237
Spanish-Style Rice, 233
Spring Risotto, 236
Simple Hoisin Chicken, 140
Skewered Shrimp Scampi, 175
Skillet Roasted Potatoes with Pork and
    Wilted Arugula, 121
Slaw, Broccoli, 53
Slow cooker dishes
Asian Pork Sandwiches, 52
Beef Stroganoff, 102
Black Beans and Avocado on
    Quinoa, 186
Bourbon-Glazed Cocktail Sausages, 6
Caribbean Pork Chili, 204
Cheesy Vegetable Pasta Alfredo, 180
Chicken and Cornmeal Dumplings, 142
Chicken and Portobellos with
    Mustard Cream, 136
Chicken Chili, 199
Chicken Tostadas, 143
Creamy Chicken Noodle Soup, 194
Crustless Spinach-and-Mushroom
    Quiche, 28
Dried Fruit, Chicken, and Bulgur
    Pilaf, 132
Eggplant Parmesan Stacks, 188
Five-Spice Chicken Wings, 7
Greek Lamb with Spinach and Orzo, 126
Italian Pork Chops, 120
Lemon-Berry Pudding Cake, 250
Lentil Taco Salad, 192
Mexican-Style Roast Sandwiches, 61
Moroccan Lamb Tagine, 125
Moroccan-Spiced Chicken Lentil
    Stew, 198
Open-Face Shredded Beef
    Sandwiches, 60
Pork Tenderloin with Sweet-Spiced
    Onions, 110
Rio Grande Dip, 16
Rosemary Turkey Roast with
    Vegetables, 150
Saucy Pot Roast with Noodles, 93
Simple Hoisin Chicken, 140
Smoked Turkey and Bulgur, 152
Texas Beef with Butternut Squash, 98
Turkey Orzo with Dried Cherries and
    Feta Cheese, 151
Smoked Turkey and Bulgur, 152
Smoky Baked Beans, 237
Smoky Nut-Stuffed Apricots, 11
Snapper Piccata, 162
Soft Chocolate Chip Cookies, 260

Soups. *See also* Stews and chili
Asian Shrimp and Vegetable Soup, 212
Cheeseburger Soup, 206
Chicken-Squash Noodle Soup, 195
Cream of Chicken and Rice
    Florentine, 196
Creamy Chicken Noodle Soup, 194
Italian-Style Lentil Soup, 208
Seafood-Corn Chowder, 214
Turkey Wild Rice Soup, 200
Vegetable Garden Soup with
    Turkey, 202
Watermelon Soup with Fresh Mint, 211
Sour Cream-Fennel Pork Tenderloins, 113
Southwest Breakfast Quesadilla, 36
Spanish-Style Rice, 233
Spice Blend, Moroccan, 96
Spiced Apple Berry Oatmeal, 46
Spiced Pear Tea, 22
Spicy Black Bean Crab Cakes, 10
Spicy Egg-Stuffed Peppers, 147
Spicy Vegetable Fried Rice, 184
Spinach
Caribbean Couscous Salad, 232
Chicken Taco Casserole, 146
Cream of Chicken and Rice
    Florentine, 196
Crustless Spinach-and-Mushroom
    Quiche, 28
Greek Lamb with Spinach and Orzo, 126
Grilled Chicken, Spinach, and Pear
    Pitas, 62
Salmon and Spinach Salad with
    Flaxseed Dressing, 85
Superfoods Salad, 89
Turkey Orzo with Dried Cherries and
    Feta Cheese, 151
Warm Yukon Gold and Sweet Potato
    Salad, 88
Spring Risotto, 236
Squash. *See also* Pumpkin; Zucchini
Chicken-Squash Noodle Soup, 195
Texas Beef with Butternut Squash, 98
Vegetable Garden Soup with Turkey, 202
Stews and chili
Caribbean Pork Chili, 204
Chicken and Cornmeal Dumplings, 142
Chicken Chili, 199
Hearty Beef and Vegetable Stew, 207
Moroccan Lamb Tagine, 125
Moroccan-Spiced Chicken Lentil
    Stew, 198
Ratatouille Stew, 210
Turkey Chipotle Chili, 203
Strawberries
Grilled Plum and Strawberry Kabobs
    with Sweet Mint Pesto, 252
Mix and Match Banana Berry
    Smoothie, 50
Strawberry-Banana Smoothies, 20
Superfoods Salad, 89
Sunrise Smoothies, 19
Superfoods Salad, 89
Sweet Party Mix, 14

Sweet potatoes
Baked Eggs with Roasted Vegetables, 29
Moroccan Lamb Tagine, 125
Root Beer-Marinated Pork Tenderloin with Sweet Potatoes, 114
Sweet Potato and Turkey Sausage Hash, 24
Turkey Wild Rice Soup, 200
Warm Yukon Gold and Sweet Potato Salad, 88

T

Tacos
Grilled Fish Tacos with Pineapple Salsa, 164
Homemade Walking Tacos, 156
Tarts
Lemon Tart with Ginger-Oat Crust, 248
Plum Galettes, 246
Vanilla Meringue Tarts, 249
Tea, Spiced Pear, 22
Texas Beef with Butternut Squash, 98
Tiramisu Shots, 253
Tofu
Bean-Tofu Burritos, 190
Breakfast Pita Pizza, 38
Poblano Tofu Scramble, 40
Tiramisu Shots, 253
Tomatoes
Bacon Tomato Melts, 56
Baked Eggs with Tomato, 32
Bruschetta Burgers, 73
Crunchy Zucchini and Tomato, 220
Roasted Tomato and Mushroom Pasta Salad, 90
Tuscan Tuna with Tomato Salad, 166
Tortillas
Asian Pork Quesadillas, 124
Bacon and Egg Breakfast Wraps, 37
Bean-Tofu Burritos, 190
Chicken Taco Casserole, 146
Chicken Tostadas, 143
Green Eggs and Ham Breakfast Burritos, 34
Grilled Fish Tacos with Pineapple Salsa, 164
Homemade Walking Tacos, 156
Lentil Taco Salad, 192
Southwest Breakfast Quesadilla, 36
Tuna and Hummus Wrap, 69
Turkey and Black Bean Chimichangas, 155
Walnut and Olive Quesadillas, 12
Tostadas, Chicken, 143
Tropical Chicken Salad Wraps, 65
Tuna
Pan Bagnat, 68
Tuna and Hummus Wrap, 69
Tuscan Tuna with Tomato Salad, 166
Turkey. *See also* Turkey bacon; Turkey sausages
Grilled Turkey Gyros, 154
Homemade Walking Tacos, 156
Italian Meatball Rolls, 66
Loaded Hash Browns, 25
Rosemary Turkey Roast with Vegetables, 150
Smoked Turkey and Bulgur, 152
Turkey and Black Bean Chimichangas, 155
Turkey Chipotle Chili, 203
Turkey Chopped Salad with Orange-Poppy Seed Dressing, 81
Turkey Orzo with Dried Cherries and Feta Cheese, 151
Turkey Wild Rice Salad, 82
Turkey Wild Rice Soup, 200
Vegetable Garden Soup with Turkey, 202
Turkey bacon
Bacon Tomato Melts, 56
Smoky Nut-Stuffed Apricots, 11
Turkey sausages
Bourbon-Glazed Cocktail Sausages, 6
Loaded Hash Browns, 25
Rio Grande Dip, 16
Sausage Skillet, 41
Spicy Egg-Stuffed Peppers, 147
Sweet Potato and Turkey Sausage Hash, 24
Warm Yukon Gold and Sweet Potato Salad, 88
Tuscan Tuna with Tomato Salad, 166

V

Vanilla Meringue Tarts, 249
Vegetables. *See also specific vegetables*
Peanut Noodles with Chicken and Vegetables, 148
Penne with Ricotta and Summer Vegetables, 182
Vegetable Garden Soup with Turkey, 202

W

Walnuts
Penne with Walnuts and Peppers, 181
Walnut and Olive Quesadillas, 12
Warm Yukon Gold and Sweet Potato Salad, 88
Wasabi-Glazed Whitefish, 160
Watermelon
Sunrise Smoothies, 19
Watermelon, Mango, and Jicama Salsa, 15
Watermelon Soup with Fresh Mint, 211
White Bean Moussaka, 189
White Chocolate Mousse, 242
Whitefish, Wasabi-Glazed, 160
Wild rice
Turkey Wild Rice Salad, 82
Turkey Wild Rice Soup, 200

Y

Yogurt
Cucumber-Yogurt Sauce, 154
Dipping Sauce, 178

Z

Zucchini
Chicken-Squash Noodle Soup, 195
Crunchy Zucchini and Tomato, 220
Italian Shepherd's Pie, 106
Ratatouille Stew, 210
Roasted Vegetable Pitas, 74
Wasabi-Glazed Whitefish, 160
Zucchini Fritters with Orange Shrimp, 178